MW00380597

# deLee Art

## The Pictorial Story of
## A California Artist and Her Company
## 1937 - 1958

Joanne Fulton Schaefer

Price Guide by John Humphries

Photographs by Ralph Schaefer

On the Front cover:

The figurines shown were carefully chosen to represent key aspects of the deLee Company history. The skunk figure was the most popular animal produced and was made in more variations than any other figure.

The World War II soldier represents the years when deLee figures were most popular and selling very well.

The little girl is a very rare figurine and represents all the hard-to-find pieces that challenge collectors today.

Finally, ***Nina*** and ***Hank*** are among the most commonly collected and loved deLee figurines.

*The valuations presented in this book are intended to be used as a guide only. Prices range widely in various parts of the country, depending on the interest in California ware. The author and publishers assume no responsibility for losses incurred using this book as a price guide.*

*Additional copies of this book may be purchased at $29.95 from:*
*Joanne Schaefer*
*3184 Williams Road*
*Butte Valley, CA 95965*
*or from your favorite antique or collectible dealer.*
*Please add $3.00 per copy for postage and handling*
*California residents must include an additional $2.17 for sales tax*

*Dealers and clubs may inquire about quantity discounts by:*
*writing to the above address or use --*
*phone — (800) 897-6263*
*fax — (530) 894-6263*



*Published by Joanne and Ralph Schaefer and John Humphries*
*Printed by IMAGE GRAPHICS, INC., Paducah, Kentucky*

**ISBN 0-9655422-0-3**

# *Table of Contents*


| | Page |
|---|---|
| Preface | 4 |
| Acknowledgements | 5 |
| Authors' Notes | 6 |
| Random Memories | 7 |
| Artist's Current Work | 10 |
| Biography of the Artist | 11 |
| Greeting Cards | 14 |
| "Ceramics For All" Excerpts | 15 |
| deLee Letterhead and Newspaper Article | 18 |
| History of the Company | 19 |
| Production Process | 23 |
| Marketing and Distribution | 25 |
| Figure Identification | 27 |
| The Collection; with Descriptions and Price Guide | 36 |
| Human Figures | |
| Baby and Children | 36 |
| Early Painting Style Young Ladies | 43 |
| Victorian Young Adults | 46 |
| Victorian Ladies | 61 |
| Dapper Young Men | 63 |
| Mexican, Oriental and Dutch Couples | 65 |
| Angels, Madonnas and Nativity Set | 70 |
| World War II Military Figures | 73 |
| Farm Children | 75 |
| Nursery Rhyme | 76 |
| Clown and Licensed Walter Lantz | 77 |
| Adults | 78 |
| Large Figures | 82 |
| Animals and Birds | |
| Domestic | 84 |
| Farm | 90 |
| Wild | 102 |
| Specialty Items | |
| Banks | 120 |
| Wall Pockets and Plaque, Spoon Holder | 122 |
| Shelf Sitter and Head Vases | 125 |
| Hors d'oeuvres Servers | 127 |
| Cream and Sugars and Ash Tray | 128 |
| Cookie Jars | 129 |
| Grease Pot Set | 131 |
| Salt and Peppers | 132 |
| Lamps | 133 |
| Flower Frog and Flower Vase | 134 |
| Other Figures Marketed by deLee | 136 |
| Unauthorized Reproductions and Look Alikes | 139 |
| Care, Repair and Preservation of the Figures | 144 |

# *Preface*

*The artist, currently at work, on a commissioned piece.*

*"It is a great pleasure for me to see the photos and accompanying descriptions of over 250 of my deLee figures, all incorporated in this fine book. To learn that so many people are seriously collecting my early work was a happy surprise and to have it culminate in a book is the icing on the cake."*

Jimmie Lee

# Acknowledgements

With sincere love and appreciation to our families who are ever patient and supportive of our projects.

We would like to thank all of the following family members and collectors who have shared their enthusiasm and interest in deLee Art with us and have graciously allowed us to photograph their collections. This book would not have been possible without their cooperation:

Bernice Adair
Doug Albacete
Blythe Bacci
Carol and David Bloom
Dianna Dahl
Marty Frasinetti
Barbara Gerow
Dale Gordon
Virginia and Al Gordon
Jackie and Mike Huey
Jimmie Lee Kohl
Barbara Powell
Tana Powell
Carolyn and Bill Price
Lynn Russell
Diane Stefani
Linda Thacker
Mary Jo and Paul Weyenberg
Susan and John Winding

With special gratitude to the following people:

Lee Adair Hastings, Jimmie Lee's niece, who contributed her wonderful art talent, family photos and memorabilia, which has greatly enhanced our book;

Marty Frasinetti, whose constant interest and encouragement, and endless sharing of rare deLee figures helped make this book a reality;

Agnes Sura, whose donation of her own copy of *Ceramics For All*, used by her when she taught high school ceramics, made possible the reproduction of its various pages in this book. We also appreciate her time to edit the entire text of our book.

And last but not least, we greatly appreciate the assistance given to us by the owners of these fine antique stores:

Barb's Buygones, Durham, California;
Barbara Gore
Cottonwood Antiques, Cottonwood, California;
Carolyn and Bill Price
Whistle Stop Antiques, Ft. Bragg, California;
Susan and John Winding

# Authors' Notes

It is with a sense of awe and joy that I embarked on this task of writing the correct and definitive book about the deLee Art Company of California.

The artist and owner of the business, Jimmie Lee Adair Kohl, is my aunt. I have spent many hours with her, carefully documenting her biography and the history of her ceramic company. She has been very helpful and excited about all phases of this project.

I grew up surrounded by deLee Art pieces and, as is usually the case, took it all for granted. After all, she's family. Some years ago when my mother moved from our large home into a smaller one, most of our figurines were given away. About seven years ago, I rediscovered deLee figurines in a local antique store. Seeing these old familiar figurines brought warm memories flooding back to me. I remembered how much I had loved the charming figures. I purchased them and began a collection that now totals 175 pieces and continues growing.

As I collected more pieces and began communicating with Jimmie Lee on a more frequent basis, I tried to find out more information on deLee from available collecting books. Reading the various Bylines about the deLee Art Company, I found most of the information to be incorrect. Clearly, Jimmie Lee herself was as unknown in the collecting world as was her ownership of the deLee Art Company.

I knew then that while she was alive and still vigorously sculpting, an accurate book needed to be written about her and her wonderful ceramic figures. With this clarification of facts, she can now take her rightful place alongside the best of her contemporary California ceramic artists, all of whom have contributed so much to our collecting pleasure. These early ceramists were truly pioneers in their field and all deserve our admiration.

Joanne Schaefer

Collectibles are the focus of my professional life. I have been both a collector and a dealer in collectibles and antiques for over forty years. And, during the past five years I have hosted a radio program, airing on 200 radio stations, six days/week, that helps people answer the question, "What is this item worth?"

One emerging facet of collecting is that collectors are focusing more on specific items or specific artists/manufacturers. The reason for this is self-evident. Just the arena of California pottery companies, which, during the thirty year period from the 30's to 60's saw over 500 of them producing wares to choose from. This profusion would tax the display and financial resources of the most ardent collector.

DeLee Art has risen to the forefront of collectibility among the California ceramic companies and deserves our notice. For me, collecting deLee ceramics has become a source of great pleasure as I have learned more about the remarkable artist who built this company.

In pricing deLee ware, I have used my "wisdom of the ages." This, of course, is tempered with the many sources on which pricing is based. The valuations in this book are from auctions, price lists, shows, antique and collectible stores and malls and many weekly and monthly collectible periodicals from all sections of the USA.

These are wonderful collectibles, and as the saying goes, Enjoy!

John Humphries

# *Random Memories*

THE ADAIRS TAKE THEIR HAUL OF "SECONDS" PREPARATORY TO LEAVING FOR SAN JUAN, PUERTO RICO.

Jimmie Lee's older brother, Crutchfield Adair, also had a flair for art and drew this family cartoon in 1941.

Crutch was a naval captain serving in W.W. II. His wife Bernice, and daughters Lee and Ann, were making a military move to Puerto Rico. Jack, was Jimmie Lee's husband at that time.

In the early 1930's, Jimmie Lee created many illustrations for newspapers and magazines. She had not yet changed the spelling of "Jimmy" to a more feminine "Jimmie."

"THE KIBITZERS" July 28, 1935

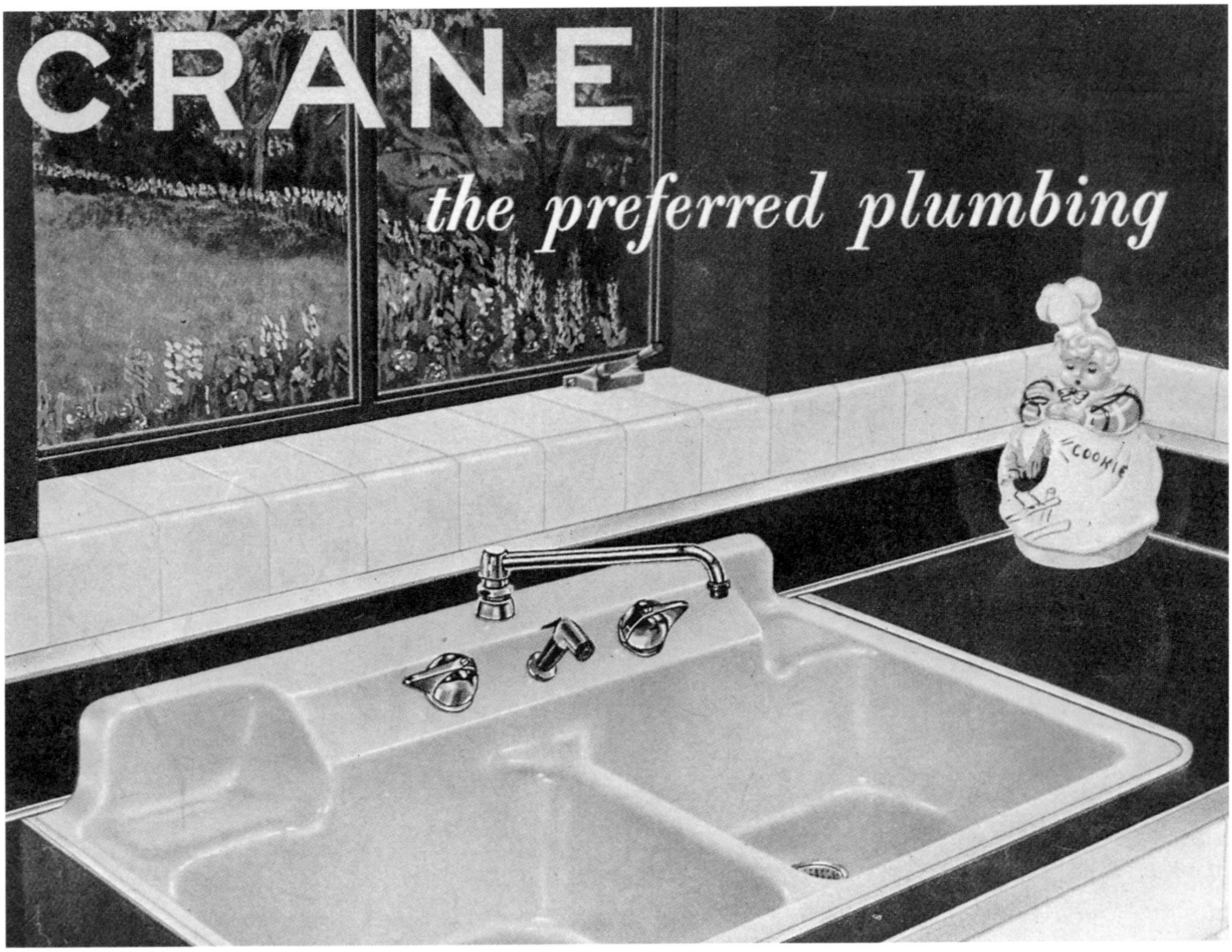
CRANE
the preferred plumbing
COOKIE

The deLee cookie jar ***Cookie,*** was used in this Crane Co. advertisement, that appeared in 'Better Homes & Gardens' April '51 issue. Our thanks to the Crane Company.

Lee Adair

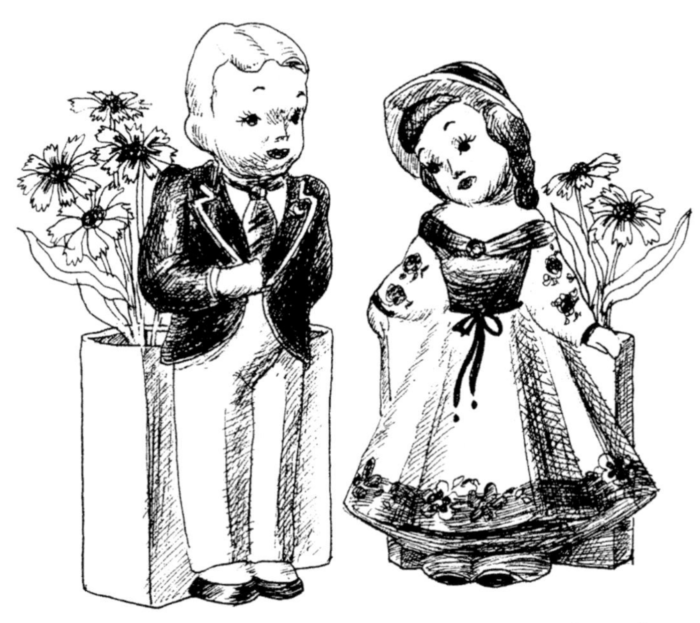

On a shelf in Auntie's kitchen,
In the quiet morning light,
In my memory shines a vision,
That brings on pure delight.

'Twas a row of deLee vases,
Dancing in a world of grace,
With slight smiles upon their faces,
Clothes done up in flowers and lace.

Girls were courted by their fellas,
Boys were held by haughty glance,
As they shown before her window,
All poised as in a dance.

In the spring she'd fill with flowers,
That would move with gentle breeze,
A warm memory of my childhood
Are these vases of deLee.

Carol Bloom, '95

# *Artist's Current Work*
## *Some Examples from 1990-1996*

This young lady is about 13" high

Bust of a good friend's son

One of her latest completed works, this bust of a now deceased young woman, sculpted from only a few photographs and her husband's memory, has been bronzed and placed in the Mauch Chunk Museum, Jim Thorpe, Pennsylvania. The young woman was a valued museum docent.

# *Biography Of The Artist*

The deLee Art Company owes its creation and ultimate success to a very resourceful and talented lady, Jimmie Lee Adair Kohl.

She was born in San Bernardino, California on March 2, 1906. She is the middle child between older twins and a younger brother. The signs of her artistic ability were evident very early in her life. At the age of five, her father, recognizing her interest, built a large 5' x 7' chalkboard for her and placed it at one end of the family porch. No one was allowed to use the board except Jimmie. She spent all of her free time drawing and writing on the board. It was her most prized possession. Around the age of seven, her love of teaching began to surface and she gathered the neighborhood children together for "lessons" on her chalk board. She taught numbers, letters and her great love, art.

Jimmie Lee and her beloved chalk board

One day, her second grade teacher asked the class to draw an umbrella. The teacher recognized her's as an exceptional drawing and showed it to the class with obvious admiration. At that moment, she remembers thinking that she would become an artist. She never changed her mind or wavered in her determination.

When she reached high school she received some kidding because her name, Jimmie, sounded like a boy's name. So, she decided to add the name "Lee" and thus feminize her name as "Jimmie Lee."

The night she graduated from San Bernardino High School, she heard that she had won the Rose Harvison Scholarship. Each year this honor was awarded to the two boys and girls in the graduating class with the highest scholastic achievement. This scholarship was the beginning of her formal art training.

Jimmie Lee's graduation picture

After graduation she persuaded her parents to send her to the San Diego Academy of Fine Arts for one year. It was an outstanding art school, conducted by a professor who had taught at the Chicago Art Institute. After a year, Jimmie Lee's father insisted that she get a college degree. She was reluctant to do so because she really wanted to pursue art training.

However, in retrospect, Jimmie Lee is grateful to her father who had the foresight to prepare her for a teaching career to fall back on. He took her to look over USC, UCLA and Pomona and let her choose. She chose UCLA since it combined the best art department with a teaching credential.

One of the first art lessons she was taught, while studying at UCLA, had a profound effect on her. An art teacher mentioned that eyelashes should never be drawn on a serious work of art. Later, she recalled this when she started making her deLee figurines and decided she would prove that teacher wrong. So, on went the eyelashes. In fact, they became her trademark used on many of the figures.

The famous deLee eyelashes

Upon graduating from UCLA in 1929 with a double major in Education and Art she took a placement test with the other candidates. She placed 2nd on the test but this was the year of the stock market crash and jobs were scarce. However, she was lucky because all four Los Angeles High Schools were looking for art teachers. She was interviewed by all of them and decided on Belmont High School. It had an outstanding, hand picked faculty and a very well-equipped art department. Ceramics was one of the subjects taught at the school. This, at a time when most people did not even know what the word ceramics meant. One person she met thought she was talking about Mexican serapes.

One small problem was that the school did not have a kiln in which to fire the finished pieces. She had to take the modeled clay pieces to a studio several miles away and pay for each firing. She also had the added burden of trying to collect this money from the students, not an easy task. When the school finally got its own kiln, she believes it was the first in the Los Angeles City Schools.

Jimmie Lee was looking for another outlet for her talent and dreamt of having a studio of her own. But kilns, supplies and labor were, of course, expensive. While continuing to teach, she started a small ceramics business. She firmly subscribed to the maxim that it's not a good idea to give up your day job prematurely. She taught at the high school for ten years.

After her business was well established, a representative from the Barnes and Noble publishing company was admiring some deLee figures in the UCLA Bookstore in 1949. He had recently been asked by his company to find a person to write a "How To" book on ceramics. He liked the figures very much and asked the store manager for Jimmie Lee's address. Her daughter, Mary Jo, a student there at the time, overheard him asking about the deLee figures. She was hesitant about giving their address to a stranger but decided that he looked professional and honest. The representative left the store and went straight to their home.

UCLA Bookstore bear

After hearing his proposal, Jimmie Lee liked the idea of passing on her vast technical knowledge of ceramics production gained from 20 years in the business. The book, *Ceramics For All*, was published in 1950 as part of the Barnes and Noble "Everyday Handbook Series" of self-help books.

In her book, one can learn everything needed to do ceramic art as a hobby, from making the original model to the final firing. It is filled with line drawings of deLee figures as illustrations of the techniques being explained (some of these drawings are shown on the next several pages). The book went through a surprising six printings. It was used as a textbook at many colleges and universities for years.

Jimmie Lee has never stopped working as an artist. As this book is being published, she is 91 years old and continues to work, along with other talented seniors, at a studio in Rogers Park, a part of the Inglewood, California, Parks and Recreation Department, and near her home. It has excellent supplies and kilns for serious ceramists. She takes private commissions for portrait sculptures that are wonderful (several are shown on page 10).

She also does some sculpting from models in her spare time, of which she has very little. Her other joys and interests in life are her daughter, Mary Jo, son-in-law Paul, and her three grandchildren, Clark Lee, Kathy Lynn and Kerry Anne.

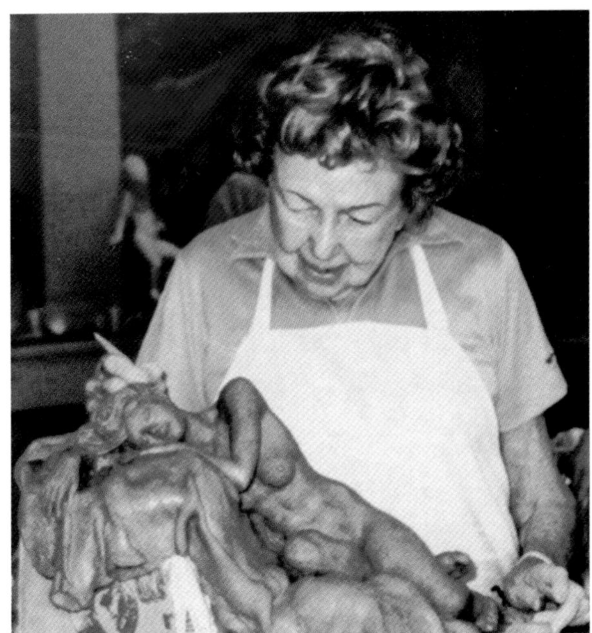

Jimmie Lee, 91 years old and 'still loving her art'.

Kudos for the book,

"CERAMICS FOR ALL"

Cable Address
BARNOBINC. NEW YORK

Telephone
ALGONQUIN 5-8100

Barnes & Noble, Inc.

B&N 1874

BOOKSELLERS • PUBLISHERS • FOUNDED 1874
105 FIFTH AVENUE
NEW YORK 3, N.Y.

April 10, 1951

Mrs. Jack Stewart
DeLee Art
734 East 12th St.
Los Angeles 21, California

Dear Mrs. Stewart:

We have just been informed that Ceramics For All will be listed among the 100 best technical books of the year in the Business and Technical Book issue of Library Journal (May 15). Congratulations!

Sincerely,

Carol Ann Luten

(Mrs.) Carol Ann Luten
Editorial Department

These are several greeting cards from a line of cards, created by Jimmie Lee and drawn from her figures. Represented here are ***Lou***, ***Happy*** the elephant and ***Stinkie***, as an angel.

The cards are shown reduced from their published size.

# CERAMICS FOR ALL

*An invaluable guide for all who want to learn about ceramics for fun or profit.*

Text and Drawings by Jimmie Lee Adair Kohl (J. A. Stewart)



they become covered with slip and are messy to handle. Also, be careful not to put a rubber band directly over the separating line of two sections. Such a band might force the two sections to separate slightly, and the slip would then pour out through this opening. This would ruin the cast, and the mold would have to be cleaned before it could be used again.

### CONSTRUCTION OF A FIGURINE MOLD

To make a mold of the skunk figurine sketched below, follow the same general procedure as described for a two-piece mold. However, more sections in the mold will be necessary to take care of the variations in the form—one for the front, and two for the back. In addition to these three sections, another one should be made of the bottom of the skunk so the figurine-to-be will have a clay base. The base of the figure looks more finished if it is made of clay with a hole (three-quarters of an inch in diameter) left near the center for casting.

**The Dividing Lines.** It is a little more difficult to place the dividing lines at the correct location on the skunk than on the vase because the form is more complicated. However, you can find where the lines should be drawn with the least amount of difficulty if you will look directly at the animal's face. The extreme edge of the silhouette that you can just see is where the line should be drawn. (See sketch.) The mold of the back of the skunk cannot be formed in one piece because the

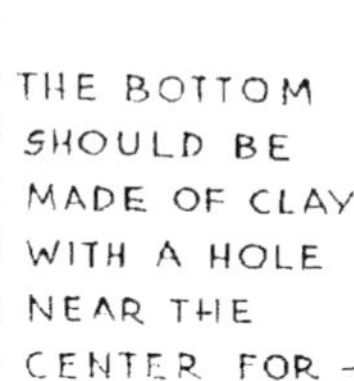

THE BOTTOM SHOULD BE MADE OF CLAY WITH A HOLE NEAR THE CENTER FOR CASTING (THIS CALLS FOR ANOTHER SECTION IN THE MOLD)

tail is in the way—one section over the tail could not be drawn loose. However, if two sections were formed for the back, they could be drawn loose by pulling to each side. (See sketch.) To locate the dividing line for the back, turn the skunk sideways and look directly at the silhouette of the profile. Again, the edge of the silhouette that you can just see is where the dividing line should be drawn. Start drawing the line at the highest point of the head, go directly down his back, along the front of his tail, over the high point, and down the back of his tail.

**The First Section.** To reduce the chances of damaging the features, make the mold of the front of the skunk first. Place the skunk with its face looking upward and with the lines that were drawn on each side exactly the same height from the table. Hold the skunk in this position by building up around him (to the dividing lines) a cradle of soft clay.

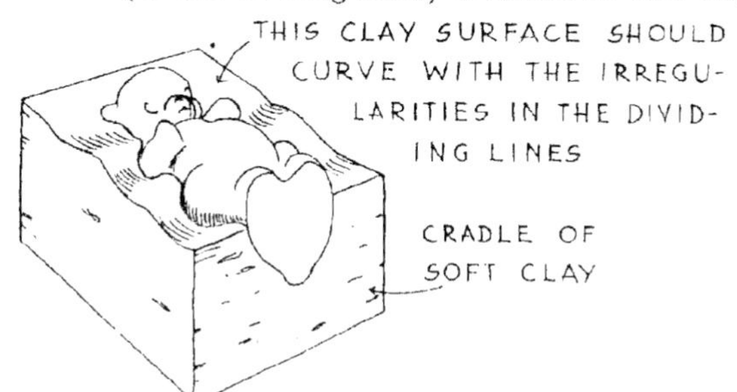


MOLD OF THE FRONT SHOULD BE MADE FIRST

**Brief Outline of Contents**

***The Model.*** Properties of clay and plasteline. Purchasing and mixing clay. Modeling by the coil method, by the slab method, and by turning on the wheel. Tools. Making an armature and a template. Wedging. Cracks. The use of mending slip.

***The Mold.*** Equipment necessary. Mixing and pouring plaster. Making bats and slabs. The construction of one- and two-piece molds and figurine molds.

***Casting.*** Two slip formulas. Mixing and pouring slip. Draining slip from molds. Opening a mold and removing the model. Pinholes.

***Finishing.*** Drying the model properly. Scraping off seams. Sanding. Sponging. Mending cracks.

***Decoration.*** Do's and don't's of decoration. Painting on green ware and on bisque. Slip painting. Sgraffito decoration. Incised decoration. Embossed designs. Overglaze painting. Decal decoration.

LOWER THE SHELF CAREFULLY ON THE FOUR POSTS

carefully lower a shelf onto the posts. However, before lowering the shelf, place little balls of modeling clay on top of each post. When the shelf is placed on these balls of clay, any irregularities due to warpage or the height of the posts will be evened out.

**Placing the Cones.** When the ware has been placed on shelves and the shelves built up to the height of a peephole

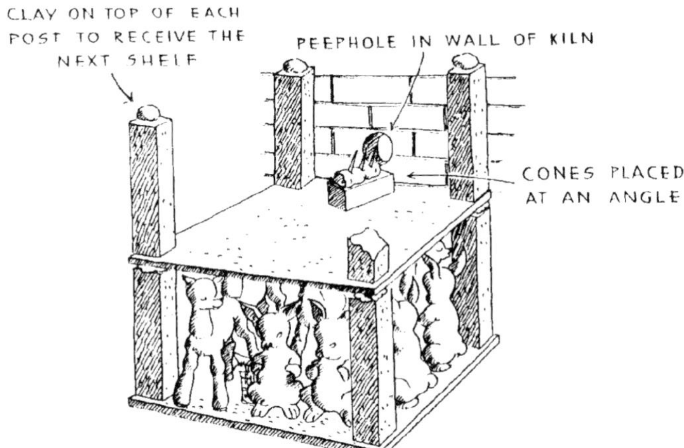


PLACING THE CONES



(see chapter on kilns, page 115), place a group of cones so they will be visible through the peephole.

The cones are formed in the shape of elongated pyramids. They are composed of very accurately compounded ingredients which melt at the definite temperatures indicated on their sides by numbers. The numbers of the most commonly used cones and their corresponding equivalents in Centigrade and Fahrenheit are given below. The equivalent temperatures are also given for slow and for rapid firing.

| Cone Number | Fired slowly (About 70° per hour) | | Fired rapidly (About 300° per hour) | |
|---|---|---|---|---|
| | Centigrade | Fahrenheit | Centigrade | Fahrenheit |
| 022 | 585° | 1085° | 605° | 1121° |
| 021 | 595° | 1103° | 615° | 1139° |
| 020 | 625° | 1157° | 650° | 1202° |
| 019 | 630° | 1166° | 660° | 1220° |
| 018 | 670° | 1238° | 720° | 1328° |
| 017 | 720° | 1328° | 770° | 1418° |
| 08 | 945° | 1733° | 950° | 1742° |
| 07 | 975° | 1787° | 990° | 1814° |
| 06 | 1005° | 1841° | 1015° | 1859° |
| 05 | 1030° | 1886° | 1040° | 1904° |
| 04 | 1050° | 1922° | 1060° | 1940° |
| 03 | 1080° | 1976° | 1115° | 2039° |
| 02 | 1095° | 2003° | 1125° | 2057° |
| 01 | 1110° | 2030° | 1145° | 2093° |
| 1 | 1125° | 2057° | 1160° | 2120° |

Usually two or three cones of consecutive numbers are selected according to the heat desired for firing the kiln. On every clay and glaze formula, the maturing temperature is always given (or should be given) in terms of these cones. For example, if you wish to fire a bisque kiln to cone 03, you should select cones 04, 03, and 02. Place these cones at a slight angle in a rectangle of clay. Be sure to dry the cones and clay before using them in the kiln. The 04 should be placed first because it indicates the lowest temperature and will bend first, then 03, and finally 02. When the 03 starts to bend, you will know that the correct heat has been reached and that you should turn off the fire. Cone 02 has been in-

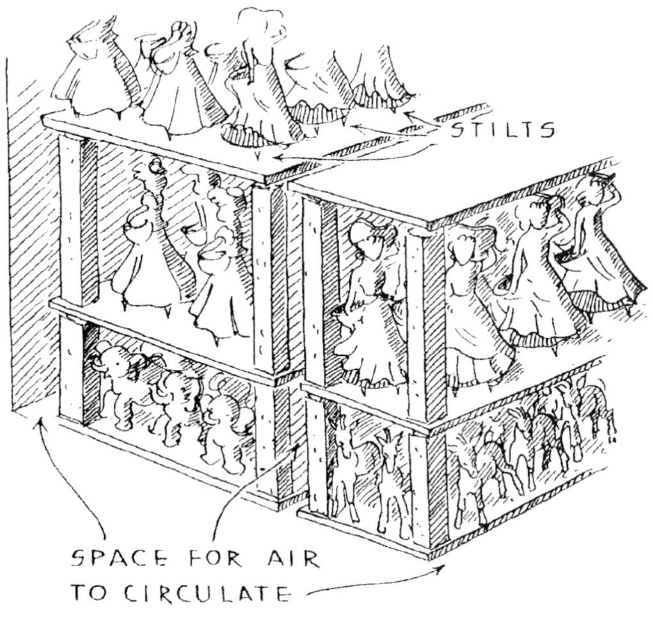


GLAZED WARE STACKED IN KILN

The ware must be stacked so that none of it interferes with the free passage of air, which must circulate through the kiln if the firing is to be even. The shelves and ware should not touch the side walls. (See sketch.)

Place four posts of the same height in position to support the first shelf and arrange the ware within this area. Each glazed piece must be separated from the next piece and the posts by at least three-eighths inch. If the piece is glazed on the bottom, it must be supported on stilts, saddles, or spurs. If such a piece is not raised on these supports, it will stick on whatever area it is placed since glaze becomes fluid in the heat of the firing. After the piece is fired and removed from the kiln, the props (stilts, saddles, or spurs) drop off and leave tiny marks on the base. These are smoothed off with a carborundum stone.

When the back area of the floor is loaded with glazed



ware, place a little ball of modeling clay on top of each post. Then brush the first shelf with a whisk broom and paint it with the solution of kiln wash *on one side only*. Next carefully lower the shelf onto the posts with the painted side downward. The glazed ware below the shelf should not come closer than a half inch. If a piece touches the shelf above it, it will stick to it when fired. If there is more than half an inch between the ware and the shelf, a lot of space is wasted. The clay balls even any irregularities in the height of the posts or any variations in the shelves.

Continue loading the ware at the back of the kiln in the same manner.

When the ware has reached the level of a peephole, place the proper cones inside the kiln in such a way that they will be visible through the peephole. Finish loading the back end before you start on the front of the kiln. Load the front the same way as described above. Place groups of cones in front of each peephole. Close the door and seal with modeling clay mixed with a little grog. The grog is not absolutely necessary, but it keeps the clay from shrinking too much.

FIGURINE SET ON STILT PREPARATORY TO FIRING IN GLAZE

**Firing.** In most ceramic plants, the pieces are bisque fired before they are glazed and then are fired again. This second burning is called the *glost*, or *glaze, burn*. The purpose of the glost burn is to melt the glaze and to unite the glaze and clay body.

The glost firing requires less time

LOS ANGELES
NEW YORK

5413 WEST WASHINGTON BOULEVARD · LOS ANGELES · TELEPHONE OREGON 0731

Los Angeles Times

SUNDAY, AUGUST 11, 1940 PART IV

# The Women of the Week

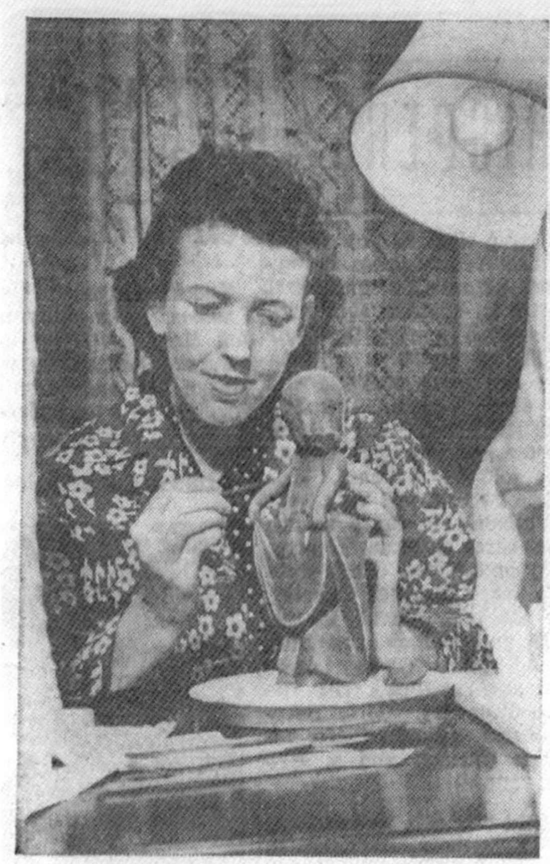

SCULPTOR — Mrs. Jack Stewart.

Recognition has come to two Southern Californians selected out of a field of some 16,000 outstanding women. This morning we salute Jimmie Lee Adair Stewart, who in private life is Mrs. Jack Stewart, and Mrs. Gregg H. Lifur (Nellita Schlotte.)

Phi Mu national sorority awarded the art and athletic medals of achievement to Mrs. Stewart and Mrs. Lifur, respectively, for their contributions. Jimmie Stewart, a U.C.L.A. graduate, taught ceramics in a local school for several years before striking out for herself to found what is now a thriving industry. Her clever little pottery figures, which she molds from clay, may be found in shops throughout the United States as well as in foreign countries. She is as versatile as she is industrious and never seems to run out of ideas for her figures which consist, largely, of tiny men and women tagged with their own names—and cunning little animals. There's many a collection of her handwork about town.

Mrs. Stewart's factory has grown to a full-fledged business with more than 20 regular employees, but she still continues to design her own molds and participate, actively, in the work. Most any day you might find her in slacks or a smock with her auburn hair pushed back from her face—hard at work in the factory.

Creators of Sculptured Ceramics

5413 West Washington Boulevard : Los Angeles

Jimmie Lee designed the company logo in 1937. The letterhead is shown at the top of this page and the envelope design at right. The figure being modeled above is shown on page 83.

# History Of The Company

To begin an understanding of the deLee Art Company, it is important to know the derivation of the name itself. The name "deLee" comes from combining two words. As noted earlier, Jimmie Lee gave herself the middle name of "Lee" in High School. The "de" portion has two sources; "d" for Hal Davidson, Jimmie Lee's attorney and original partner and from the French word "de" meaning "of" or "by" as in "of Lee."

The company began with a small investment and a large dream. Jimmie Lee enjoyed teaching, but from the beginning she wanted to start her own company and to create the hundreds of figures that had always been in her imagination.

In 1936, she was involved in a small automobile accident. Her attorney obtained a cash settlement for car damages and injuries. She took the money, $165.00, formed a partnership with the attorney, and began the long, bumpy economic road to success. Eventually, after many years, the fledgling business grew into a successful company.

They borrowed more money and found a little shop in the Huntington Park area of Los Angeles with only one kiln, but possibilities. That arrangement lasted only 30 days as the location and shop proved unsuitable. They moved the business to another nearby community where there was a building with three kilns, none of which was working properly as it turned out.

Recollections of early problems were provided from an article about Jimmie Lee in a 1939 Los Angeles Times Article, "Odds and Ends of Life" by David Winston. She is quoted as saying, "We found ourselves paying $50 a month rent, about $200 to helpers, $54 to the gas company and, in two months of that expense, we didn't have a piece of merchandise that we would dare to sell. I would stay out there all night and work with our formulae. I'd watch the kilns too, and try to make them function properly. It all might seem hopeless and yet we were so full of hope. I'd get a quick shower when morning came and go on to school to do my teaching; then rush back again in the evening and start pushing the pottery through. It always flopped."

They abandoned the poorly working kilns and moved again to another part of town. Another pottery maker told Jimmie Lee and her partner that they could use a small part of his factory. He had a tunnel kiln, a special oven where the ware was sent through on cars. The tunnel kiln was even worse since it had faulty second hand parts and broke down frequently. It was consistently too hot and melted everything.

The worst was yet to come. Jimmie Lee managed to get a few good samples out of this tunnel kiln. Her partner took them to the New York gift shows and received 500 orders which she could not fill! The kiln owner had gotten tangled up with some serious litigation and the Sheriff came and shut the place down. It didn't matter that the deLee Co. was only a renter of space. She was not allowed to move out a single figurine. "I couldn't even get my molds and my models until an attorney managed to get a release for me. By then it was too late. My partner had to return from New York."

The indefatigable entrepreneur, Jimmie Lee in her office

They had lost the 1936 Christmas business. Without any money, they somehow managed a $200 loan for a second hand kiln. They were then able to move back to the earlier site, set up the better working kiln and start all over again. Even then the colors were bad and the glazes faulty, causing the finished pieces to craze. The partners hired a chemist who worked on Jimmie's time, used her materials and also demanded $200 for each glaze. They told him to keep his glazes because they could not afford that outrageous sum.

It was up to Jimmie Lee to figure out a solution. She experimented with hundreds of glaze formulae and even hired a chemist at $1 an hour just to listen to him talk. Every minute that she could spare from teaching, she was working on glazes. By the time she figured out what was needed, the Christmas business of 1937 had come and gone. "This time I wasn't afraid. I knew that my formula would work, including some five different essentials combined in secret proportions. There's nothing strange about that 'secret' business when you talk ceramics. Every pottery house guards its glazes with utmost care. Mine isn't even written down on a piece of paper. I make every drop of it myself and not even my employees today (1939) know what it is.

Jimmie Lee on a rare vacation trip

"My partner, though, began to get discouraged by the summer that followed that tragic 1937 Christmas. I bought him out by assuming his half of our debts. By then, we were operating a plant out on Washington Blvd. near Culver City."

By the end of 1938, Jimmie Lee's success finally began. In January of 1939 her company produced 3500 saleable pieces. "January was even better than December because the merchants began getting more calls for my pottery." It was the glorious beginning of having to keep up with the demand for deLee Art pieces. With her new found success came new pressures. Up to twenty full time employees worked in the factory with schoolgirls coming in part-time to assist. Even with all this help, she struggled to meet the demand for her products. Her pieces were selling very well in the United States and foreign markets.

However, other serious problems were yet to come. In 1941, when the United States entered World War II, any company not directly related to the war effort suffered an immediate employment freeze. The Company then had 12 employees. As business improved steadily, they desperately needed more people to keep up with the orders pouring in but they were not allowed to hire more. All ceramic companies were affected.

During this time, there were over 500 California pottery companies all busily producing a huge variety of distinctive wares. Names such as Kay Finch, Barbara Willis, Hedi Schoop and Braytons of Laguna Beach are all familiar to collectors. The employment freeze was a serious blow to all the companies because it prevented them from increasing their business. In addition, the pottery business was very labor intensive. For this reason, Jimmie Lee decided to borrow some money from another relative and move part of the deLee Company to Cuernavaca, Mexico, where she could employ as much help as needed.

It was very difficult doing business in Mexico because of the tendency of employees to take advantage of an American employer. She struggled for several years to keep the factory running but good, reliable workers were scarce and kiln repairs were difficult. It was impossible to get the necessary materials in Mexico and when, after lengthy delays, materials did come from the States, the sacks were broken and the contents practically unusable.

Her intent was to produce the figures in Mexico and ship them to the United States for sale. They ended up selling some figures in Mexico but never produced enough to ship many to the U.S. Fortunately, the plant in Los Angeles continued to produce well with the limited staff. By 1944, the plant in Mexico was abandoned and all production concentrated in Los Angeles, operating with limited personnel until War's end.

With production labor so scarce, store buyers were desperate to have products to sell. Jimmie Lee tells of having some of the buyers from Los Angeles stores like Bullocks and Robinsons come to her factory at night to help unload the kilns, label and pack figurines. For this effort, Jimmie Lee would be able to allot them more pieces to sell! These were difficult times.

From 1944 to the late 1950's, the deLee factory hummed along making high quality figurines for the gift marketplace with Jimmie Lee leading the company until the end.

The end came in the late '50s when several hundred California pottery companies were put out of business due to the rising trade of foreign and domestic fakes and reproductions.

Jimmie Lee cited a specific example of this problem. A famous catalog company in Chicago, that is still active today, sold 25,000 deLee wall pocket skunks named "DeStinker," in one season. All of a sudden, deLee Art did not receive any more orders for the skunks, even though the deLee wall pocket was shown in the following season's catalog. Jimmie Lee sent for one of the catalog skunks. Sure enough, it was an unauthorized reproduction taken directly from her original piece. It was selling in the catalog for the same price but was of poor quality. Clearly, the catalog company was making a better profit with the change.

For the deLee Company, as well as hundreds of other companies, these unauthorized reproductions were impossible to fight. The cost of litigation was too high and the fakes were popping up everywhere. Usually, the buying public was unaware that they were purchasing fakes. The deLee factory had to be closed and Jimmie Lee turned her artistic talent in other directions.

Jimmie Lee in the finishing room, May 1939

# The Glaze

Glaze is a glasslike substance that is put over a clay piece to add beauty to the object and to make it more or less impervious to water. The simplest glaze would be composed of lead oxide and silica—1 part silica to 3.7 parts lead oxide. However, this would make a very crude, yellowish glaze —one which would be too fusible under most heat conditions and which would lose its gloss if left in the kiln very long. Alumina counteracts these faults, but it is expensive and difficult to obtain. Fortunately, clay contains alumina, is inexpensive, and is plentiful, so clay is added. From this simple beginning, potters have gone on to develop beautiful, well-balanced glazes of every imaginable kind.

### KINDS OF GLAZES

**Clear Glazes.** Glazes can be clear or oqaque, shiny or mat (also called *matt*); they can be colorless, or color can be added. The most basic, perhaps, is the clear glaze.

### DEFECTS IN GLAZED WARE

It isn't often that a novice will select a glaze, clay body, and firing schedule that are so perfectly blended that the ware will come out without defects of some kind. Here are some of the principal faults and how to overcome them.

**Crazing and Shivering.** Several things affect the successful outcome of a glaze. The most common fault is too great a variation between the coefficient of expansion and contraction of the glaze and body. When the glaze contracts more than the body, the glaze is under a tension which causes it to form tiny cracks, called *craze*. In the opposite situation, the glaze cracks because it is too large for the body. This type of cracking is called *shivering*. If the shivering is extensive, pieces of the glaze will peel off.

There are many other causes of crazing and shivering. The bisque may be underfired or overfired. If the bisque is underfired, the crazing may not appear when the piece is first removed from the kiln. After a few weeks or months, the cracks will appear and grow worse upon standing. If the bisque is overfired, the cracks will have been formed before the ware is taken from the kiln and will not develop further.

If the glaze itself is underfired, very irregular and broken cracks result. Some appear to change direction without meeting other cracks.

Crazing and shivering can also appear when both the body and glaze are correctly fired but when there is an inherent disagreement. The glaze might mature at cone 03 and the body at the same temperature, but if the body shrinks too much, for example, the glaze will not fit it, and the result will be disastrous. To correct such inherent faults, the composition of the glaze or body would have to be changed.

In most cases, the addition of silica ($SiO_2$) will prevent crazing, and the decrease of silica will prevent shivering.

*To give you an appreciation for the difficulty of the ceramic process, here are a few problems that can happen with just the glazes alone, from the book,*
**CERAMICS FOR ALL**

**Underfiring.** Underfired ware can be spotted by the condition of the glaze. All these defects are indications of underfiring: crazing (mentioned in detail above); pinholes and scum on the glaze; gas bubbles or blisters on the glaze. The last defect indicates that the bubbles in the glaze did not have enough time to escape properly. Gas bubbles or blisters can be eliminated either by a longer firing period or a longer soaking period.

**Overfiring.** When ware is overfired, underglaze colors and colored glazes will fade and often run. Overfired glaze usually crazes, and extensively overfired ware will warp or even collapse.

**Dark Spots.** Minute particles of metal which may have fallen into the glaze or clay body will show up as strong, dark spots after the firing. Since these dark spots give the ware such a displeasing appearance, you should use no metal anywhere in the process of preparing the clay and glaze—no metal spoons, no metal containers, etc.

**Discoloration.** If the ware is not fired immediately after it is glazed, dirt may accumulate on it. Clean the piece thoroughly before firing if it has been allowed to stand around for any time at all after the glazing; otherwise it may come out of the kiln discolored.

Tiny bits of refractory material from the kiln walls, ceiling, or shelves sometimes become loose, fall on, and stick to the ware. This can be avoided by brushing the kiln and shelves carefully before loading and by painting the walls, the floor of the kiln, and one side of the shelves with a kiln wash.

**Bare Spots.** If a glaze contains too much flux, it will run and leave bare places on the ware. This running can be eliminated by adding a little clay and silica to the glaze.

**Runny Colors.** Some colors, such as those containing cobalt, will run (because of the nature of the oxide or carbonate forming them) unless a little refractory material such as silica is added to them.

**Dry Spots.** Dry spots in the glaze are usually present because the potter carelessly rubbed some of the glaze off. However, bisque often has a hard spot which is difficult to glaze. This hard spot is formed by the concentration of salts where the slip first hits the mold. (See page 61 for one way of avoiding this.)

Colors containing refractory materials absorb some of the glaze. The absorption causes a dry spot on the colors. Ware that has been painted with underglaze colors always requires more glaze than plain bisque ware.

**"Bright" Mat Glaze.** If mat glaze is applied too thin, the glaze will brighten when it is fired. Use a thick coating of mat glaze. If the glaze will not go on very thick, add more of the binding material. (See page 98.)

Mat glaze will also brighten if the firing is reducing (see page 113) or too high.

# Production Process

The meaning of what constitutes a "ceramic" piece was explained by Jimmie Lee in ***Ceramics for All***. "The words ceramics and pottery are used interchangeably today (1950) among laymen. Actually, ceramics means anything that has been fired in a kiln; pottery, brick, enamel, glass, sewer pipe, terra cotta, and tile. Pottery is just one phase of ceramics. It refers to ware made of clay." The deLee Art Company of California concerned itself with the production of pottery figures which, because they were fired in a kiln, became ceramic figures.

Jimmie Lee's talent and influence operated throughout the entire production of deLee figures. With only a few exceptions, she modeled every figure made. She used a modeling clay called Plasteline or Plastecine, an ancient compound. It is a prepared clay made of ball clay, lanolin and glycerine. It never hardens and does not shrink. For these reasons, it cannot be fired.

She found it difficult to concentrate and create her unique figures during the factory day, so she usually did her modeling (the sculpting process) at home in the evening.

Jimmie Lee employed a master mold maker from England, Mr. Longbothom. It was his job to make an accurate, workable master mold. Jimmie Lee recalls, "He really knew his craft. He had his own area in my factory. No one was allowed to touch his sink, tools or sponges. One of the reasons for my success was his wonderful molds."

The master mold was made from the original plastecine model in as many pieces as needed. A working mold was then made from each piece of the master mold so that all of the working molds would produce sharp figurines. Each working mold can make approximately 100 casts after which it is discarded. Each time a mold is poured, a microscopic layer of the mold wears off, eventually causing a loss of fine detail. (See photos above-right)

The 'deLee Art' and other information incised on the bottom of most pieces was carved in the master mold by Mr. Longbothom. After removal from the molds, the green ware (unfired clay) was dried for several days in a special drying room where heat and drafts can be controlled. After drying, the mold seams were removed. If the seams were removed when the cast piece was still damp, the knife marks would show through the glaze in the finished piece.

Fresh, new mold — Same dog, older mold

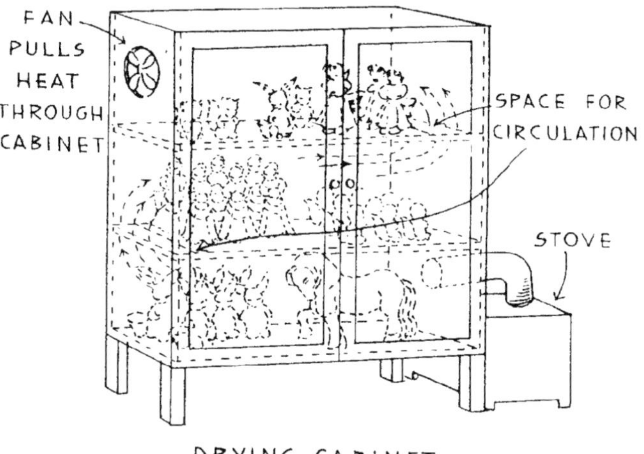


DRYING CABINET
(from ***Ceramics for All***)

Although the art of creating the figures through modeling was the crucially important first step, the next step, the painting of the figure while still in the dry green ware stage, was also extremely important. It was here that the unique charm of deLee figures was added.

The artists were usually obtained by newspaper advertisements. They came in and painted samples for Jimmie Lee to demonstrate their ability. If they were good enough to be hired, they received on-the-job instructions about the deLee methods. There were 6 to 20 painters working all the time. They were paid by the piece and so working quickly was essential. Jimmie Lee tells of one very good artist, Ruth Konigsberg, who only lasted one day because she painted beautifully but not nearly fast enough to keep up with production. Years later, Ruth and Jimmie Lee were in the same art class at Rogers Park. One day they were talking and Jimmie Lee mentioned deLee Art. Ruth replied that she was the one who had been fired after one day. They have been good friends ever since.

Jimmie Lee and her head painter mixed all of the deLee colors. They remained consistent for the 21 years of production and help identify deLee pieces today. However, she was never able to get a bright red where parts of the red paint didn't turn gray upon firing. She has just recently learned why she was unable to fire red and wishes that she had known this 50 years ago! She explained that when firing a bright red, the kiln must have only glazed pieces in it for that firing as the red is in the glaze, not in the paint. If any green ware pieces were also in the kiln, the red glaze will turn spotty grey. This was not a well known fact in the 1940's. Collectors will find this a helpful hint today because pieces that are said to be deLee but have bright red fired on them cannot have been produced at the deLee factory. There is further clarification of this statement in the Figure Identification section.

With each new piece to be painted, Jimmie Lee, or her head painter, would paint a sample to give the staff painters an idea of what was expected. Beyond this, they were given some freedom as to how each piece would be painted. They were talented artists themselves and needed some space for creativity. For this reason, collectors will find the same figure painted in many different designs and color schemes within the deLee color palette. The retail stores and florists wanted the figures to be painted differently as well.

After painting, the figures were placed on special trays or shelves fitted with posts and stacked in the kilns for firing. The first firing is called a Bisque firing. From the 1930's through the 1950's, most pottery factories, including deLee, were using the low firing technique for their wares. Low fire refers to the temperature achieved inside the kiln for the duration of the firing process.

The deLee factory generally used a Cone 04 for the bulk of their work. Cone 04 translates to 1,992 degrees Fahrenheit. From the Glossary of ***Ceramics For All***, "Cones are elongated pyramids composed of very accurately compounded ingredients which melt at the specific temperatures indicated on their sides by numbers." By placing these cones inside the kiln and watching them through peepholes, the potter can determine the temperature inside the kiln. If you want to fire at Cone 04, you place Cones 03, 04 and 05 inside the kiln in front of the peephole. When 04 begins to soften and bend over, you have achieved your ideal temperature and can then turn off the kiln.

Ceramics For All

CONES PLACED IN CLAY

It is a very complicated process to blend all of the various elements of ceramics together and come out with an excellent product. Jimmie Lee worked years to perfect her glazes so that the figurine and the glaze would mature at the same time in the firing process thus producing a craze-free piece. Glazing was accomplished by taking the pieces to a special spray booth where the secretly formulated glazes were applied with a spray gun. The pieces were then returned to the kilns for a second and final firing, the Glost firing, which permanently sealed the piece.

Jimmie Lee closely supervised all procedures at the factory, personally training each employee to her satisfaction. At the height of production, and before and after the restrictions imposed by World War II, there were 30-35 employees.

From 1937 until the end of the War, the factory was located at 5413 W. Washington Blvd., Los Angeles. After the War, they moved to 734 E. 12th Street, Los Angeles, where they remained until the factory closed in 1958.

# *Marketing And Distribution*

The deLee Art Company did not sell direct retail, only wholesale to gift buyers for outlets such as department stores, gift shops and florists. All production done at the factory was to fill orders received from these customers. One store that consistently ordered hundreds of pieces was Little America, the tourist and truck stop in Wyoming. From this one source alone thousands of deLee figures traveled to new owners all over the United States.

To reach potential buyers, the company employed a variety of marketing methods. One method was to put new items on display for buyers at major gift shows across the United States, especially New York. Also, a booth in the Los Angeles Gift Mart was maintained throughout the year. New items were also placed in trade magazines for buyers to consider. In addition, the company had several salesmen who traveled all over the United States, showing the new samples and taking orders. They also solicited refill orders as necessary.

This method of showing products required a catalog. The company produced a simple, straightforward catalog every six months, consisting of one or two sheets of deLee letterhead (see page 18). Around the border of the paper, Jimmie Lee added line drawings of the figures that were presented in the catalog. Down the middle of the paper was a typed list of the names, descriptions and wholesale prices of the pieces currently available. Orders taken by the salesmen or over the phone were done using this catalog. Jimmie Lee and Jack Stewart, her husband at the time, did much of the selling themselves.

The original price of a collectible is always an interesting topic. For their time, deLee ceramics were in the affordable range. The retail price for the human figures and large animal vases ranged from \$1.50 - \$3.00, and the animals from \$1.00 - \$1.50. In the 1950's, the company produced the larger, more complicated figurines such as the Siamese, Latino and Cuban dancers and the Hawaiian pair which sold for more, around \$4.00-\$6.00 each.

If a particular figure did not receive enough orders and/or was not reordered, it was discontinued as soon as possible. This accounts for the scarcity of some pieces.

With several exceptions, all figures sold by the deLee Art Company were modeled by Jimmie Lee. These exceptions are discussed and shown in "Other Figures Marketed by the Company."

A delightfully true story that she vividly remembers concerns a New England gift store. They did an entire front window of their store using only deLee skunks hanging by colorful ribbons. It was a traffic stopper. The shop sold so many skunks that they were able to burn their mortgage. They sent a telegram to the factory stating, "SEND MORE SKUNKS QUICKLY!"

*The many faces of deLee Art . . . . . .*

*it wasn't just about eyelashes!*

# *Figure Identification*

Due to circumstances beyond anyone's control, all of the company's records and catalogs were destroyed about six years ago. As a result, reconstructing the various numbers of figures produced is impossible. Jimmie Lee has tried to remember as much as she can but 40+ years is a long time. She believes that approximately 350 unique figures were modeled.

**POPULARITY**

There is no doubt that the best selling figure was DeStinker, the skunk wall pocket for matches, used in the bathroom before deodorizers. This figure sold upwards of 100,000 total including 25,000 to one catalog company alone. The DeStinker production was so large that three other ceramic companies were commissioned to make them for deLee.

***DeStinker***

Of the total product line, the deLee company made more variations of skunks than any other single figure type. When asked why so many different skunks were made, she replied simply that they were great sellers. The company constantly moved with the market-place.

Many of the pieces crafted by the deLee Company were vases. Most of these vase figurines were sold to florist shops. At one point, the florists were asking for larger figures that could hold more water and flowers. Responding to this need, the company developed a line of larger animal vases, one of which is shown on page 93, the Animal section of The Collection.

As it is with most good artists, Jimmie Lee has a style all her own. As one sees and collects more pieces of deLee Art, it becomes possible to recognize her style. Experienced deLee collectors tell us that they can "spot a deLee clear across a crowded salesroom." Therefore, this chapter seeks to help the less knowledgeable collectors with basic recognition of deLee pieces that they may want to add to their collections.

**DISTINCTIVE CHARACTERISTICS**

One descriptive word keeps coming up with deLee collectors. They speak about the charm of these figures. When modeling the figures, Jimmie Lee never tried to make them an exact model of the real thing. She carefully and skillfully made a simplistic version of the figure, this giraffe for example, leaving out a lot of realistic details. The poses of each piece are creative and when painted, complete the total package of a charming and attractive piece. It is more artistically difficult to know what to leave out than what to add on.

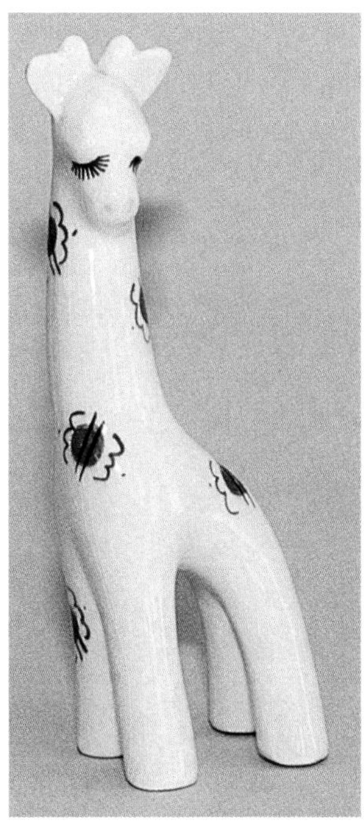

***Tops*** in his simplistic glory

In the years following WW II, she realized that the marketplace was demanding a more realistic and detailed art. Always responsive to customer attitudes, she began a line of large, very detailed adult figures, most of them dancers. They can be enjoyed on pages 78-80.

**PAINTING TECHNIQUES**

One of the first things that identifies a ceramic piece is the colors that are used. On most of the figures the natural clay color was the background and the decorations were done mostly in pastel shades of pink, yellow, blue, green, lavender, etc. Where necessary, black and brown were also used. Most of the figures came in natural white clay color or pink skin tone. The use of these colors remained more or less the same throughout the years of production.

Most of the first pieces created during 1937-40, have a tiny, thin line of brown paint creating lace and dots on the girl's dresses. The flowers are tiny and simple and few different colors are used. The overall feeling of the piece is white. Excellent examples of this early painting technique are the figures shown on pages 43-45. As the years went on, the decorative design became much more elaborate and colorful. Sometimes the artist painter would just put a "wash" color on for hair and other times the hair would be painted solidly.

Except for the airbrushing technique, deLee figures were all handpainted by artists. It should be noted that fine airbrushing also requires a great deal of talent and skill.

A cute bunch of 1950's deLee bunnies. They range in size from 3-4½". They are airbrushed with features painted by hand.

**LABELS**

The first, albeit elusive, help in identification, comes from the labels. Every deLee piece produced left the factory with a company label and a name label, with one exception. Ceramic figures that were not sculpted by Jimmie Lee usually were not given a name but had a deLee logo sticker applied before sale. An example of this are the 12 Siamese cats sculpted by another artist but produced and sold by deLee. Owners through the years have washed off or otherwise removed many of these labels.

The company label came in several forms. The most common was a 3/4" round silver paper label with a black art deco design that reads "deLee Art, California, hand decorated." This label also comes in a 1/2" size for smaller figures. There was also a very rarely used rectangular silver paper label. The one example that we have found was unreadable. The rarest label was used on pieces made while the factory was haltingly working in Mexico. This label is a 3/4" silver paper label and reads, "deLee Art Co, Cuernavaca, MEXICO." Examples of all these labels are shown on pages 30-31.

The style of the figures' name labels remained the same throughout the years. It was a long, narrow, rectangular silver paper with the chosen name for that character printed in black. One time, the label company ran out of silver, so for a short time they used gold. Jimmie Lee and her husband, Jack, made up all of the names. Many of the names are funny, like the pigs Grunt and Groan, which fits with her great sense of humor. It's a treasure hunt to finally find one piece that still has its name label, then we all know the name for our similar figures.

A few of the characters also came with an additional label. The first is a 1" x 2" red paper oval. On one side is the address of DE LEE ART, and on the other is a funny poem about the piece. We have found two figures so far with this label, DeStinker and HorseDurves. Their labels are on pages 122 & 127. Super Stinker came with a different extra label. It is a 4" long "Gold Ribbon" made out of paper. It states "First Prize Super Stinker" and includes a funny rhyme. On the back is the company's address. This example is on page 106. Jimmie Lee believes there are a few other figures that also had additional similar labels.

**INCISED MARKINGS**

Incised markings are the next helpful item in determining an authentic deLee piece. As noted earlier, the incised marking was inscribed in the master mold so it always showed up on every piece produced from that mold. Incised means "to cut into; to carve or engrave." Not every piece of deLee was incised, so this method of identification cannot be used alone. Sometimes, as the mold was used frequently, the incised mark is blurred and impossible to read.

There has been some discussion among collectors as to why a commonly found figure like "Nina" carries a 1940 or 1941 incised date when we know they were produced for years because there are so many of them. The answer is very simple. Mr.

Longbothom incised the date into the Master Mold when it was first created. Many working molds were made from this Master Mold through the years (one working mold for about every 100 figures produced), but the Master Mold, with the date on it, did not change. Thus, a figure that was actually produced in 1949 could well have been from a 1940 Master Mold. If a particular figure was popular, they kept making them for years.

The animal figures with four freestanding legs are rarely incised because there is no logical place to put the mark. There are some two-legged human figures not on a base and freestanding birds that present the same problem.

Most of the incised markings include the copyright symbol (©). Jimmie Lee never registered the copyright of any of her pieces. It was too much trouble. She was told by a friend that just using the symbol would help to protect her designs for about one year. That was good enough for her purposes since she usually had all new designs a year later anyway. Photos and line drawings of deLee incised markings are shown on pages 32-33.

A key identification point to note is the base of the figure where the incised markings (if there are any) are located. The deLee Company made solid bases to their figures. Obviously, the ones that are planters had to have a solid piece for a base. A few of the non planter figures have a hole in the bottom but they still retain a large area of base. If there is no base piece at all, it probably is not a deLee.

## PAINTERS MARKS

The painters at the deLee factory were encouraged to add their "Painter's mark" on the bottom of every piece that they completed. The mark was usually the first initial of either their first or last name. Pages 34-35 show examples of these marks. One letter that is seen frequently on many different pieces is the letter 'E'. Jimmie Lee remembers that a couple of painters were with her for the 21 years of production. Surely, this painter was one of them. Be advised that not all authentic pieces of deLee have a painters mark, as it was not required of the painters.

## UNDER GLAZE CRAZING

To complete our discussion of identification, it is necessary to mention under glaze crazing. If you look closely at many of the pieces, you will notice tiny, fine lines under the glaze. This crazing has occurred over the last 40 years due to climatic conditions. Jimmie Lee says that it happens to some pieces and not others because of the figure's relative position in the kiln when fired. Some of the pieces were in a slightly cooler area of the kiln and took the glost firing a little differently. This crazing is very common and does not affect the value of the piece unless the lines have darkened and become very obvious.

To sum up this Section, you have this intangible thing called the "deLee Look." After you see and study many pieces, you will become an expert at finding "The Look."

***The Nativity*** by Jimmie Lee Stewart

This photo was used on the cover of Jimmy and Jack Stewart's Christmas card of 1946.

The figures are the prototypes for the production nativity set on page 72.

# *Labels*

The company used three subtlely different round silver labels through the years. This is the first label used from 1937 to about 1944. Notice that all of the letters in "deLee Art" are filled in with solid black.

This is the second label. The size and basic Art Deco design are the same but only the 'A' in "deLee Art" is filled in with solid black. This one was used from about 1944 to about 1951.

Finally, we have the third label. This one came in two sizes, ¾" and ½" in diameter. Obviously, the small one was used on the smaller pieces. Notice that none of the letters are filled in with solid black. This one was used from about 1951 until the end of production in 1958.

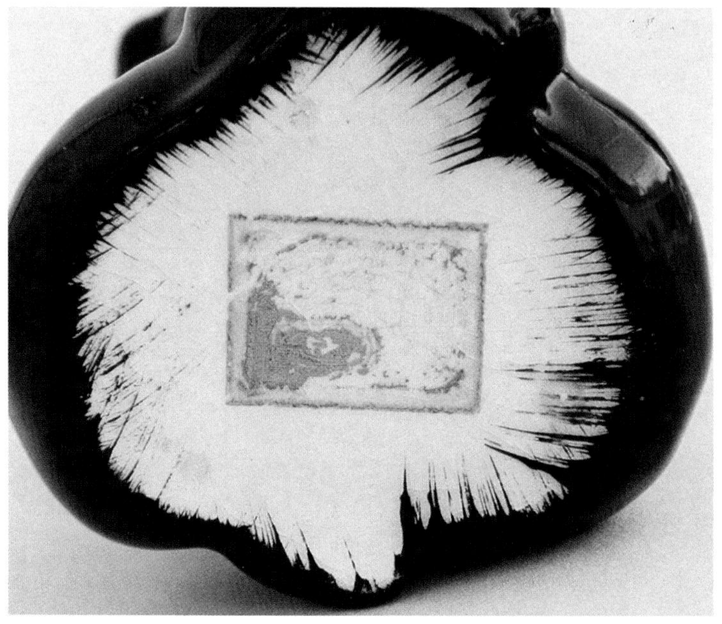

This is a very uniquely shaped label for deLee Art. None of us knows what it looked like originally. This is the only one we have seen like it.

These are the various marks used in the Cuernavaca, Mexico production. Congress passed a law in 1891 which states that all products manufactured out of the USA must be marked with the country of origin before importation into this country. This applies even if the company is American. As stated in the text, very few figurines made it successfully out of the Mexican factory.

One of the earliest incised markings. At this time, the name of the figurine was also written on the bottom.

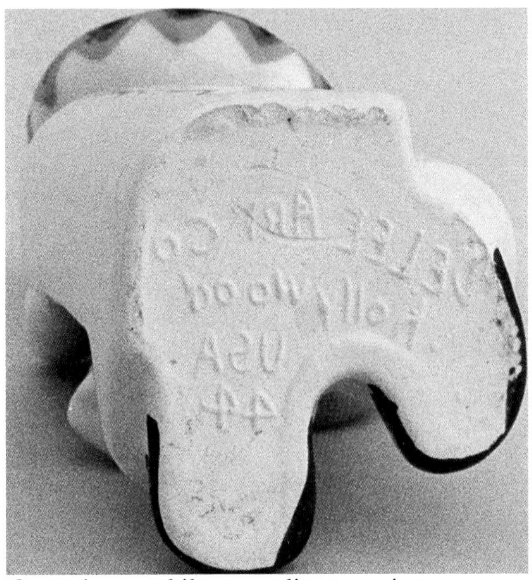

Once in a while, gremlins got into production and the base plate was applied inside out. Instead of being a concave inscription, these were convex. The biggest problem was that the writing was backwards, as seen here. When held up to a mirror, it reads correctly.

In the early 1940's, Jimmie Lee had a license with the cartoonist, Walter Lantz, to create a few of his characters in ceramics. This is the base of ***Andy Pandy***.

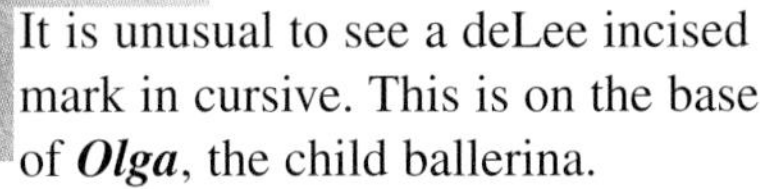

It is unusual to see a deLee incised mark in cursive. This is on the base of ***Olga***, the child ballerina.

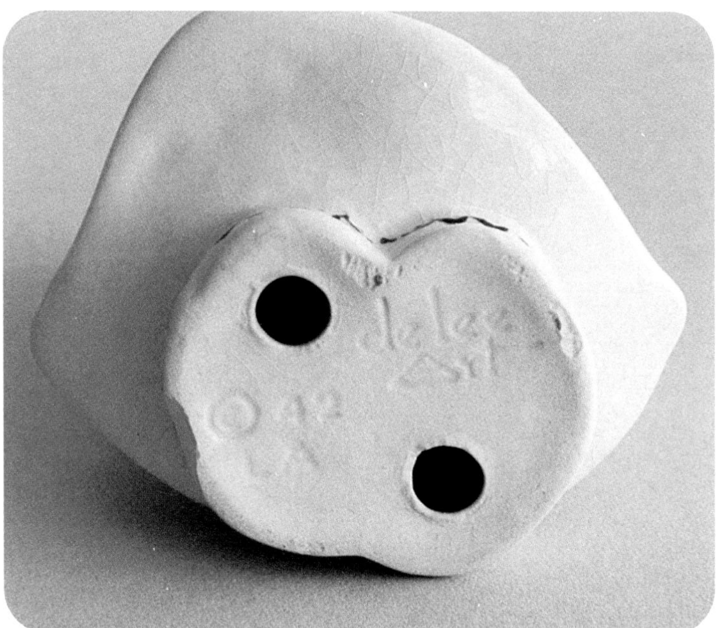

In the 1950's, the company began using this different and simplified mark. Some pieces were stamped, as shown below, while others were incised with the mark.

These three figurines have typical deLee Art incised markings. The mark was incised (carved) into the master mold, usually by the Master Moldmaker, Mr. Longbothom. All working molds made from this master would, of course, carry the same mark.

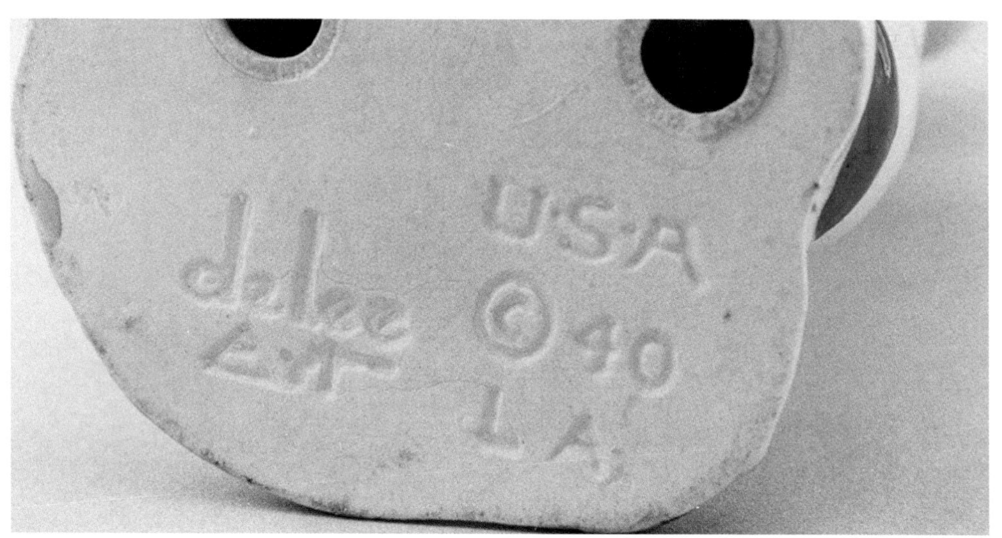

# *Painters' Marks*

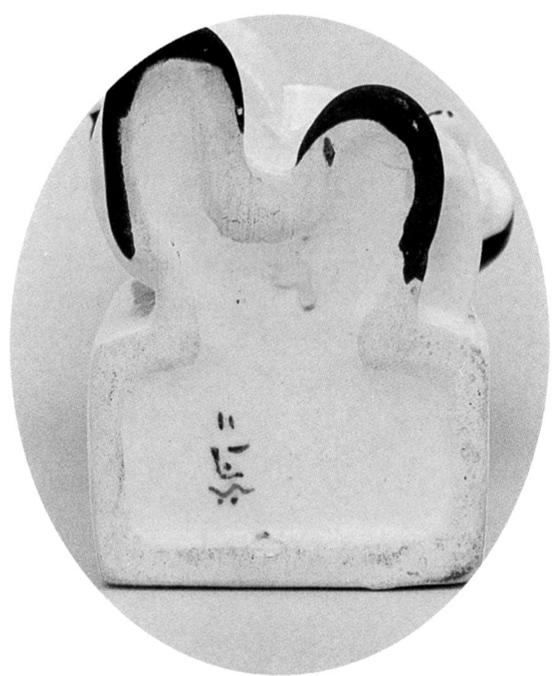

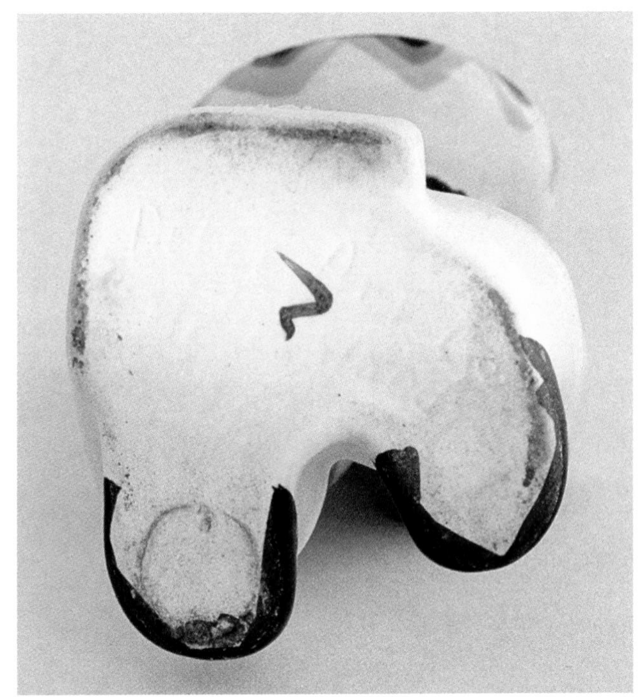

Through the years, the company employed many different painters. Some of the ladies stayed for years, others did not. All of these people were artists in their own right and were encouraged to put their mark on their work. These are just a few of the marks. The mark was the first letter in either their first or last names. The 'E' mark appears on a large number of figurines produced throughout the entire 21 years of production.

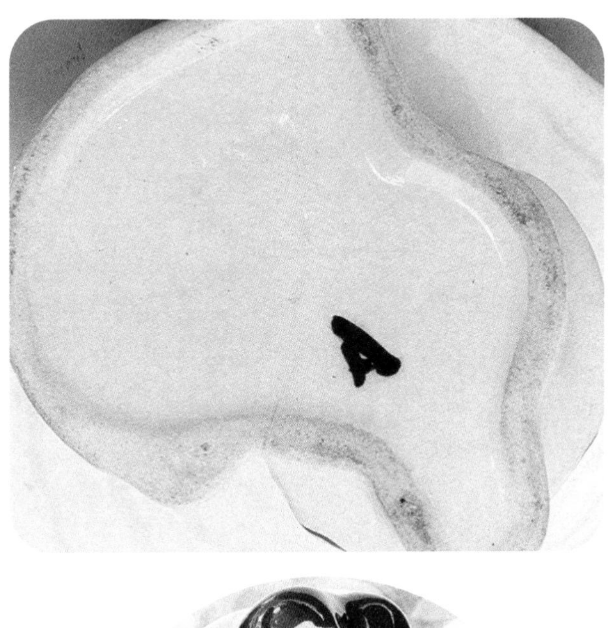

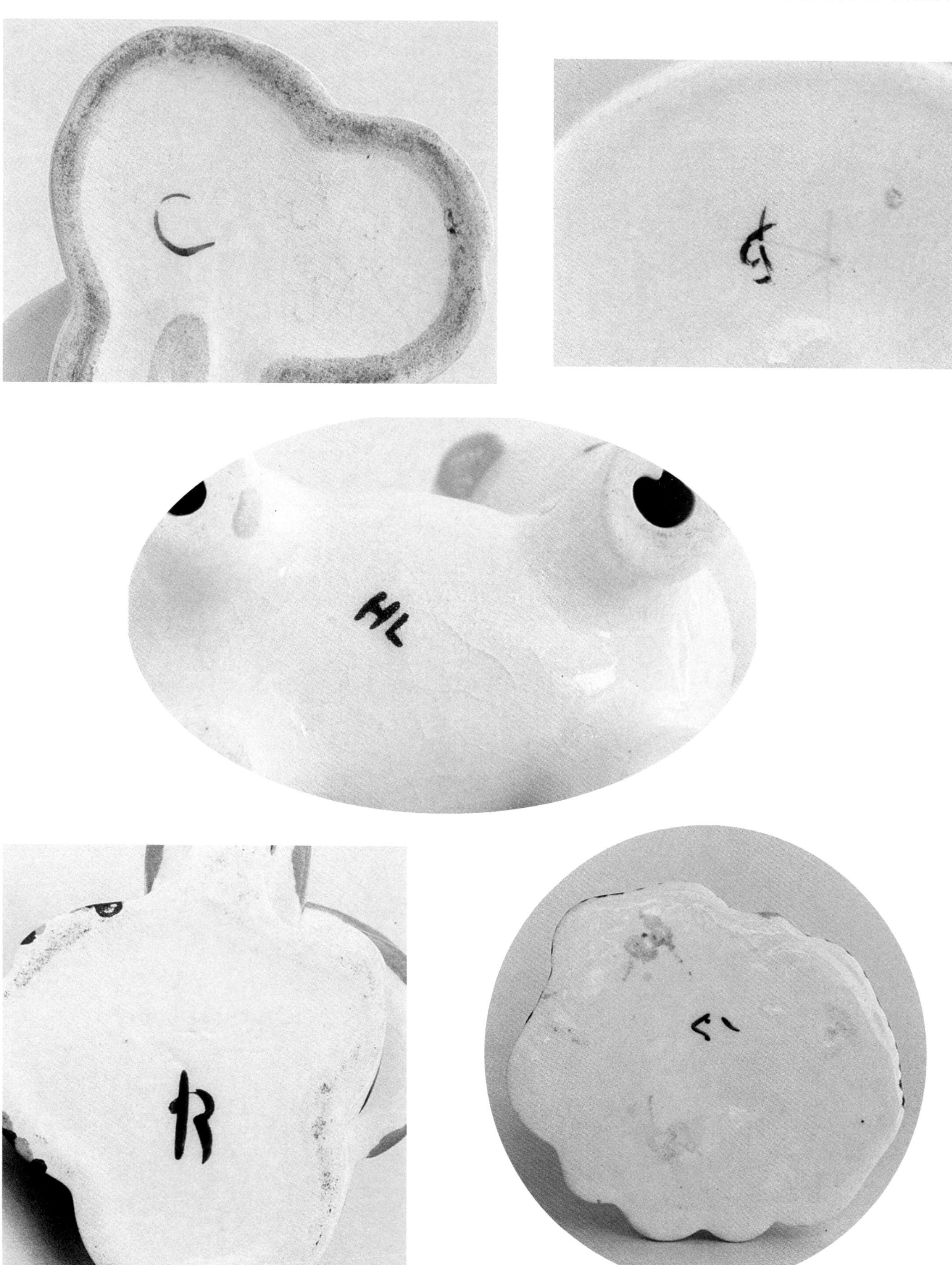

# The Collection
## With Descriptions and Price Guide

Throughout this book, most of the descriptions start with a number in bold parenthesis. These numbers relate directly to the pricing information. A given number will stay with its particular figure for all future price guides. New deLee figures (those not seen by the authors prior to the publication of this book) will be given a new permanent number. These numbers will provide a consistent reference for this and all future pricing information. The estimated values in this book are based on figurines in good condition with no breaks or chips.

**(1)** 3½" baby with large open blue eyes. Incised 'deLee Art, 39 © LA'.
Estimated value: $65-85

**(2)** 4" boy with sailboat. He has a round silver deLee sticker on his back.
Estimated value: $65-85

**(3)** A darling pair of little girls who have fallen down while roller skating. The photo on the right shows their back side. They are 4" long; are not incised and do not have labels.
Estimated value each: $65-85

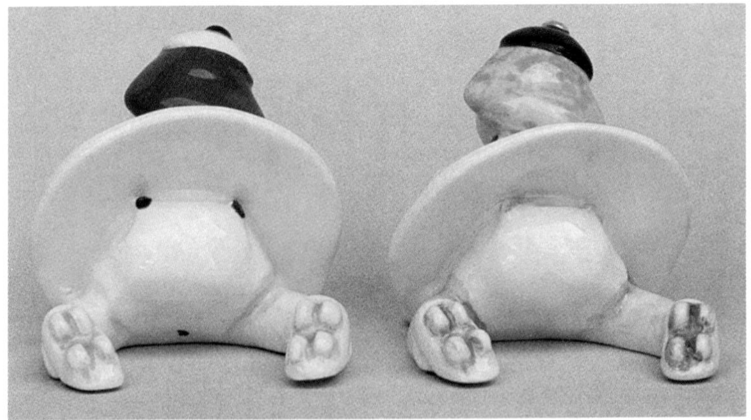

There are more little ballerinas in different poses in this series.

(4) 3½" ballerina Olga; incised 'deLee Art' in cursive on the bottom.
Estimated value: $65-85

**(5)** This little girl, ***June,*** is 4" tall (seated). She has an open book on her lap with a giraffe on the right side and a hanging plant on the left side. She has her name plate.
Estimated value: $65-85

**(6)** 5" little boy with his dog, molded together on the same base. He is not incised and carries no labels.
Estimated value: $65-85

A darling pair of children. ***Mandy*** is 6" and has a round label. ***Moe*** is 4½", has a round label plus his name label, and also sports a darling pose.
Estimated value for ***Moe*** (**7**): $65-85
Estimated value for ***Mandy*** (**8**): $65-85

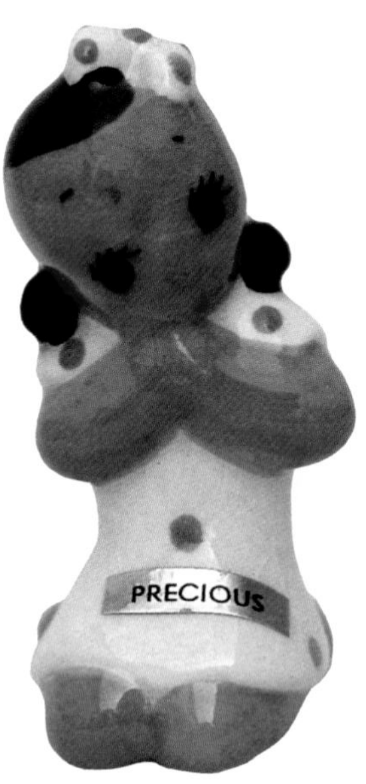


(**9**) ***Precious*** is a kneeling, 3½ high figure, with her name label and deLee sticker on the base.
Estimated value: $65-85

(**8**) This 6" ***Mandy*** has a round, silver label and the name label. She is incised deLee Art USA.

**(10 and 11)** These two children might be a pair as his bow tie matches her hair bow. He is 7½" tall and is incised 'deLee Art LA © 40 USA'. She is 6" tall and has a 2" dog molded to her. We do not know their names.Their rear views are found on the back cover.
Estimated value for the girl **(10)**: $65-85
Estimated value for the boy **(11)**: $65-85

**(256)** This little girl with a doll is 3" high seated. She is incised 'deLee Art © 39 USA'. She has great little balls of hair.
Estimated value: $65-85

**(257)** ***Corny*** is 5¼" tall and has a deLee sticker on the bottom and a ***Corny*** name tag. His original price of $1.95 is also on the bottom of his foot. He has 1 fish on a line in his left hand and 2 fish on lines over his right shoulder. His rear view is on the back cover.
Estimated value: $65-85

**(12)** 6" girl with a bell skirt. She has no labels or marks. Although she is the same height as some of the other figures, she has a much smaller head and slimmer body. Estimated value: $65-85

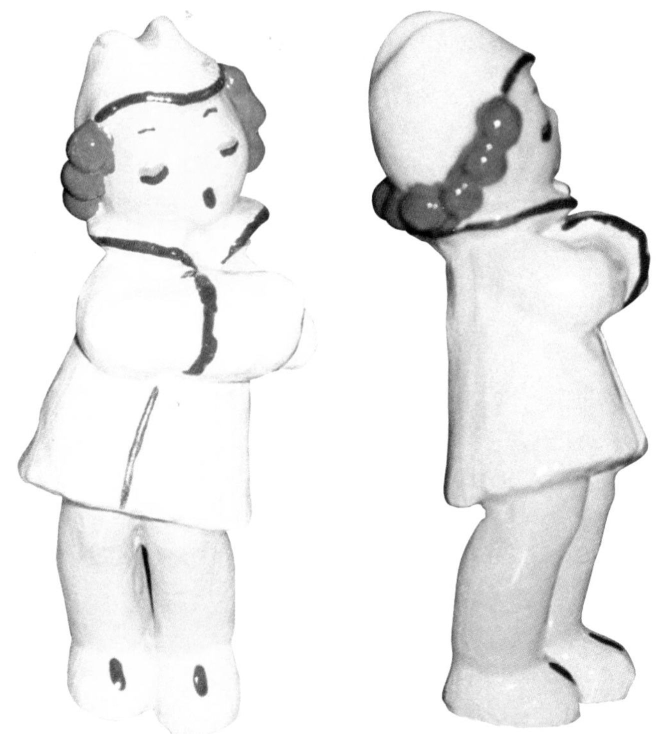

**(13)** 5¼" young girl with muff. Notice the round balls for hair, very 1940's. She is incised 'deLee Art ©'. Estimated value: $65-85

**(258)** The ***Thinker*** is 2¾" high seated. He has a deLee sticker on the bottom from the 1937-1941 period. Estimated value: $65-85

**(14)** This 5" girl comes in many different painting combinations. She does not have any labels or incised marks. Estimated value: $65-85

**(15)** 3" young girl in a prayer mode. She is incised 'deLee Art © 39 USA'. She has flesh toned paint.
Estimated value: $65-85

A blonde hair, blue-eyed version of the boy below, has a deLee sticker on his bottom.

**(16)** A flesh toned, 4" high boy in swimming trunks. The remains of his name label can be seen on his leg. The style and painting of these figures is very different from more often seen deLee figures.
Estimated value: $65-85

**(17)** 5" Football player named ***Speedy.*** He is incised 'deLee Art' and has his name label. Notice that most of the figures in this series have open eyes.
Estimated value: $65-85

**(18 and 19)** Two figures, 4" long, are ***Johnnie*** and ***Joanne***. They are two suntanned kids at the beach. They both have their name labels and deLee labels on the bottom.
Estimated value for the pair: $130-170

**(20)** This boy with his sand bucket is ***Lee***. He is 8½" tall and has his name label. He is incised 'deLee Art' and can also be found painted in deLee green.
Estimated value: $65-85

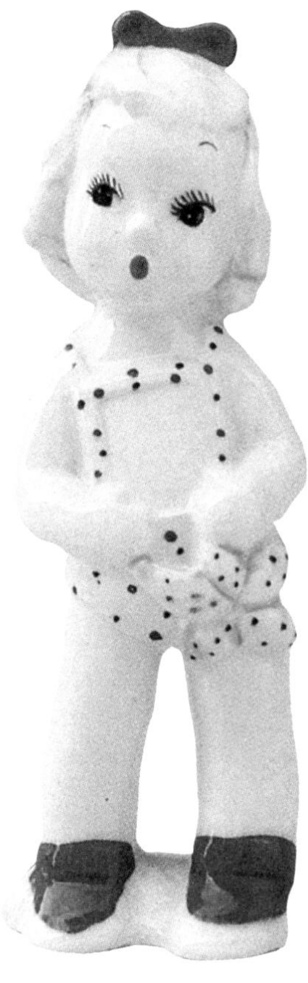

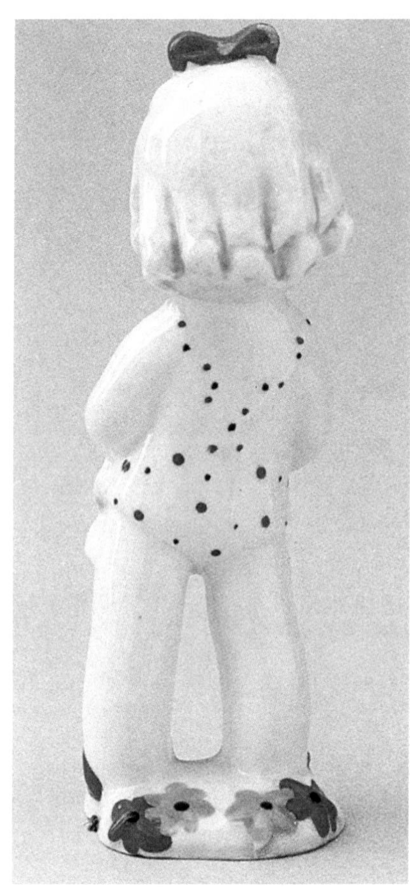

**(21)** This darling girl is holding a starfish. She is 7" and is incised 'deLee Art, USA © 40 LA'. We don't know her name.
Estimated value: $65-85

**(22)** 4" high seated girl with dress flying and a surprised look. She has a deLee label on the underside of her skirt.
Estimated value: $65-85

**(23)** ***Sally*** is a 6½" young lady holding a chick. She is incised '***Sally*** (in cursive writing) deLee Art © 1938'. Notice the tiny flowers and thin brown lines indicating trim and lace. ***Sally's*** bonnet forms the opening for the planter. Estimated value: $35-45

***Sally*** is found with three bow colors, yellow, green and blue. This brunette ***Sally*** is seldom found.

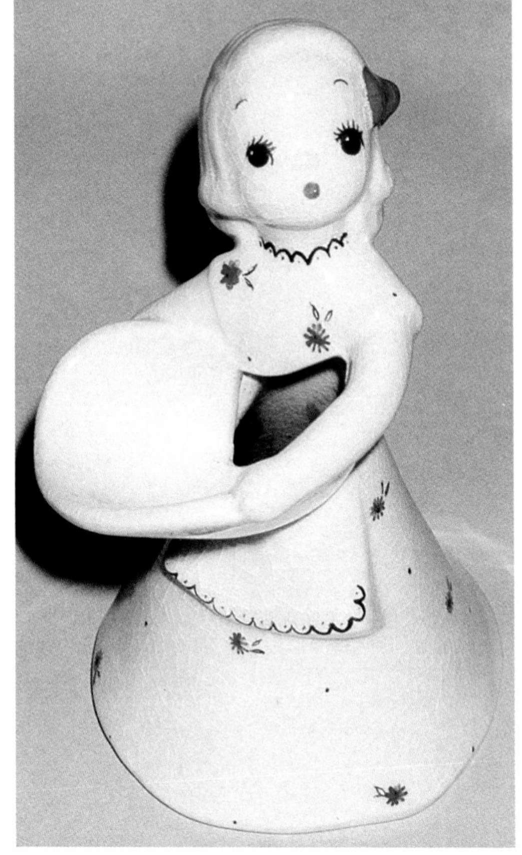

**(24)** Here we have ***Lee*** the girl. She is 8" tall and an open-eyed beauty. She is holding a large basket that is a planter opening. ***Lee*** was named after Jimmy Lee's niece, Lee Adair, who created the drawings for this book. She is incised '"Lee" deLee Art USA'. Estimated value: $45-65

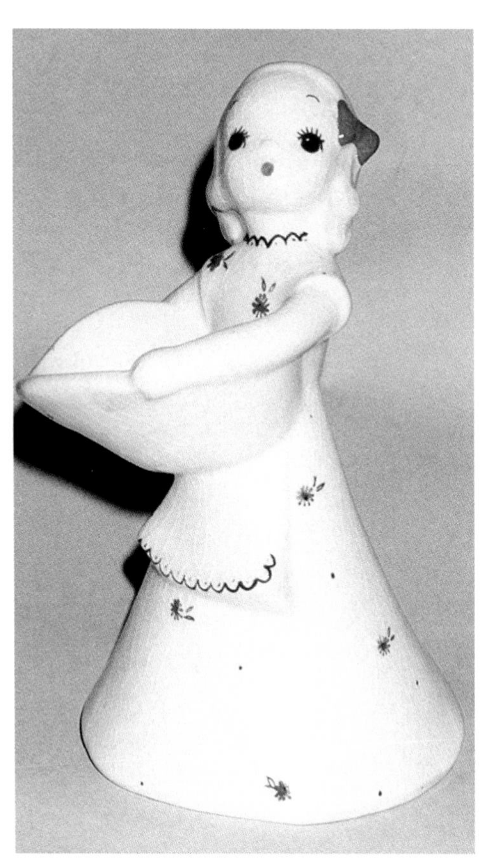

**(25)** 6½" ***Mary Jane*** is holding onto the ribbons of her hat which is behind her and forms the planter. She is shown in the green and yellow ribbon versions. She probably also came with blue ribbons.
Estimated value: $35-50

**(26)** Two differently painted versions of ***Irene***. She is 6½" tall and forms a planter opening under her apron in front. She is incised ***Irene*** in cursive writing, 'deLee Art © 1938'.
Estimated value: $35-50

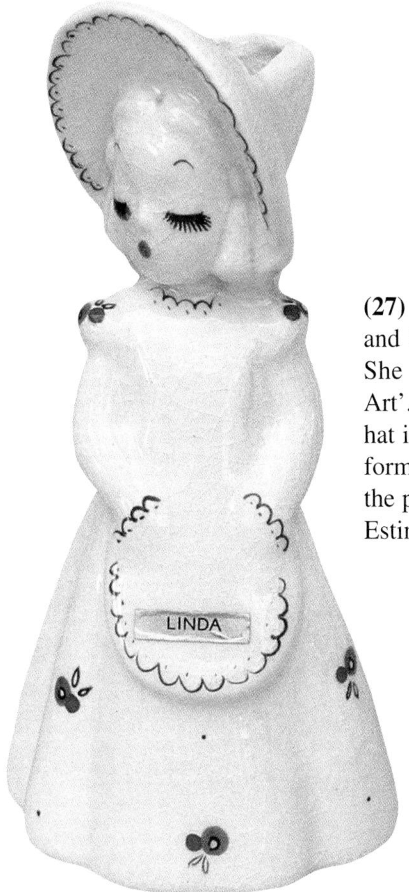


**(27)** ***Linda*** is 7½" tall and has her name label. She is incised 'deLee Art'. The crown of her hat is cut open at the top forming an opening for the planter.
Estimated value: $35-50

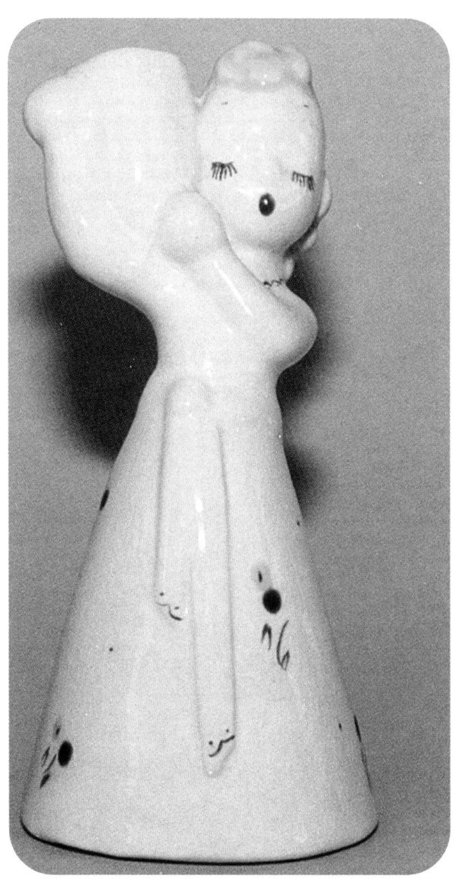

**(28)** 7" young girl holding a vase. She has no markings. The vase is the opening for her planter.
Estimated value: $50-65

**(29)** 7" ***Audrey*** is also a planter, the opening of which can be seen in the photo. She has a round deLee label on the back and is incised 'deLee Art © 1940.'
Estimated value: $40-65

**(30)** A charming young lady named ***Dimples***. We have found two different name tags for her. One is as shown here with the other being, ***Dimple***. She is 8" tall and comes in many different paint combinations. Like so many of the deLee figures, the painters were allowed the opportunity for creativity. Her dress has a bustle in back which forms a planter. All of these we have seen have the incised mark incorrectly reading 'DeeLee Art Holloywood'. Somebody must have had a bad day. Estimated value: $35-50

***Dimples*** is shown here with ***Larry***. He is a natty gentleman sitting on a planter. ***Larry*** is described in detail later.

**(31)** 7" ***Sally*** is incised 'deeLee Art Hollywood'. It is unknown why the "dee" is misspelled. She has a round deLee label and her name label. She is leaning on a planter behind her.
Estimated value: $35-50

**(32)** ***Daisy***, shown above, left and right, is 8" tall and has a planter in front formed by her dress folds. She comes in a variety of painting combinations. All these ***Daisies*** are incised 'deLee Art, Hollywood © 1946'.
The ***Daisy*** on the left, accompanied by ***Dude*** who will be described later, has a round deLee label on the bottom.
Estimated value for each: $35-50

**(33 and 34)** ***Kitty*** and ***Kenny*** are 7" tall. They are both planters. His planter is behind him and hers is in her bonnet. They come in a variety of painting styles. Besides the white clay base, they also come in the pink tone base as shown above. The pair at left have their name labels. They are incised 'deLee Art, Hollywood, © 1947'. Estimated value for the pair: $80-95

**(35)** ***Hattie*** is one of the most commonly found figures, indicating a large number produced. She is 7½" tall and is incised 'deLee Art, Hollywood © 40 LA, USA'. Her name is also written in cursive on the bottom. She is shown here in just a few of her many painted variations. Her planter can be clearly seen.
Estimated value: $30-45

There are so many pretty ***Hatties*** to enjoy, we decided to show a few more. Here she is shown with ***Hank*** in his matching color outfits. Notice the couple on the bottom right of the page, they are in the pink toned base color.

**(36)** This ***Hattie*** has **Mexico** painted on the bottom. Her painting style is slightly different and she has open eyes. She probably was made in the limited Mexico production.
Estimated value: $45-55

**(37)** The young lady with the beautiful picture hat is ***Annabelle***. She is 8" tall and is incised 'deLee Art, Hollywood © 41, LA, USA'. The figure on the far right is painted in the early style. It appears that in 1941, they were using some of both painting styles.
Estimated value: $35-45

**(38)** Our young lady with her parasol is ***Patsy***. She is 7" tall and has a planter clearly seen. Notice that she comes with open or closed eyes. She is incised 'deLee Art, Patsy, 1942' on the bottom. The figure shown at top left and center is especially beautifully painted.
Estimated value: $35-45 each

**(39)** ***Sue,*** with a bouquet, is 8" tall and comes in many different painting combinations. Shown here, her basic color is white or pink tone. The ***Sue*** on the left has a painter's mark on the bottom and ***Sue*** on the right has a sticker on the bottom. Her planter is behind her.
Estimated value: $45-60

**(40)** ***Lou***, who is 7" tall, appears to be inspired from a nursery rhyme. She does not have any markings and is a planter.
Estimated value: $35-50

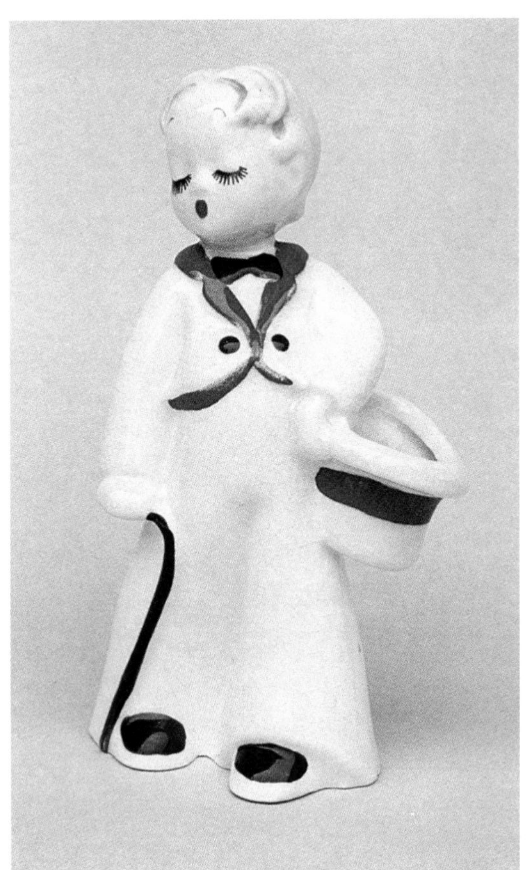

**(41)** This young man's name is as yet unknown to us. He is incised 'deLee Art USA, 1939', and is 7" tall.
Estimated value: $45-60

Although these two are not necessarily a pair, they look quite handsome together. Both of them are planters.

At the top left is a very unusual ***Johnny***. He does not have the pillar/planter behind him to his waist. His right hand and rear pants are completely modeled and only a remnant of the pillar is present.

**(42 and 43)** ***Joanne*** and ***Johnny*** are special as they are named after the author and her brother. Several of the family children's names were used on figures. ***Johnny*** is 8½" and ***Joanne*** is 8". 'deLee Art' is incised on the bottom of each. Notice that ***Joanne*** comes with open or closed eyes. They are both planters.
Estimated value for each: $45-60

**(44)** Most deLee collectors agree that ***Nina*** is the most commonly found deLee human figure. Production covered many years and was obviously very popular. Her apron is a double planter. She is 7" tall and comes in a wide variety of painted versions. Some of the lovliest and most creative painting styles are found on ***Nina***. She is incised 'deLee Art 1940', and on others, '1943'. Estimated Value: $25-40

Another opportunity to enjoy the wide variety of painting colors and patterns used to create ***Nina***.

***Nina*** is shown here with ***Danny*** (top left) and ***Hank***. It appears that ***Hank*** is often painted to be ***Nina's*** partner.

**(45)** ***Pat*** is 6¼-7" tall and incised 'deLee Art, © 1940 LA, USA'. The planter is formed by her uplifted skirt. Notice the detailed painting on her pantaloons. It is interesting that the earliest ***Pat*** shown on the right above, is noticeably smaller than the others. Estimated value: $25-40

**(46)** ***Maria*** is 7½" tall and is a planter. ***Maria,*** above left, has a deLee round sticker on her base. She is shown below with ***Larry*** who is painted to match her. They come in both white and pink tones. Estimated value: $30-45

**(47)** ***Lizzie*** is 9" tall and is lovely in her picture hat. She has a planter behind her on the right side. She also comes in a variety of painting patterns, including pink toned skin and with open eyes. She is incised 'deLee Art, © Hollywood, 1949', and carries the 'E' painters mark. Estimated value: $35-50

A rare open-eye version of ***Lizzie***.

Three appealing young ladies that appear to have been made at the same time. They make a fine set. All three are planters and all are more difficult to find than many other deLee figures.

**(48)** ***Lou*** is 8½" tall and is partially seated on her planter. She is incised 'California deLee Art' and has her name sticker.
Estimated Value: $50-65

**(49)** ***Maisie*** is 9" tall with a parasol. She has her name sticker and a fancy 'Y' painters mark. She is the most difficult to find of the three.
Estimated value: $55-70

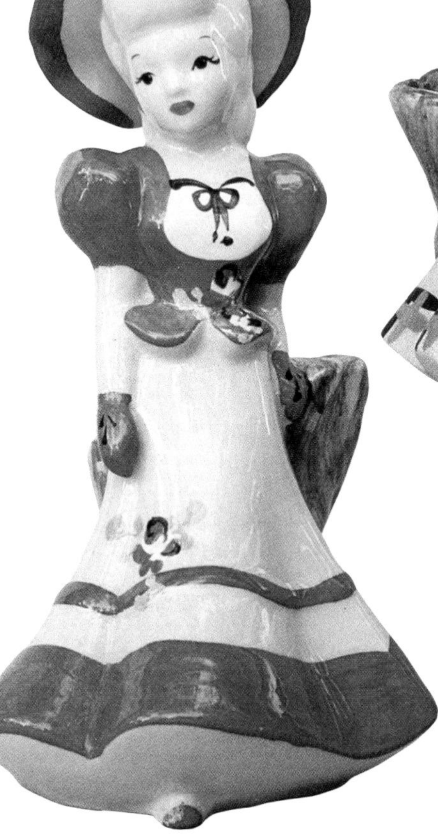

**(50)** ***Patsy*** is 9" tall and is incised 'deLee Art, Hollywood © 1950'. She has the 'E' painters mark. Her back view is shown at right.
Estimated Value: $50-65

**(51)** ***Hank*** is a very self-assured young man, standing 7½" tall. He is casually leaning against his planter which is behind him. Represented here are three different painting styles. Hank is incised 'deLee Art 1943' with the 'A' painters mark. Hank also comes in pink skin tones. Estimated value: $35-50

The ***Hank*** on the right sports a very splendid pair of plaid pants and the typical spats. He is incised 'deLee Art © 1943' and carries his name label.

Here's ***Hank*** dressed in soft pastel shades. His painting schemes always go with matching girls, many of them ***Nina***.

**(52)** ***Sonny*** is 8" tall and is standing in front of a large planter. His round deLee label is on the back of the planter. Estimated value: $50-65

**(53)** Seated ***Larry*** is 7½" tall. His planter is behind him. He is incised 'deLee Art, Hollywood, 1940 ©'. Notice this fellow has open eyes. Another Larry with closed eyes and pink tone is on page 60 with ***Maria.***
Estimated Value: $50-65

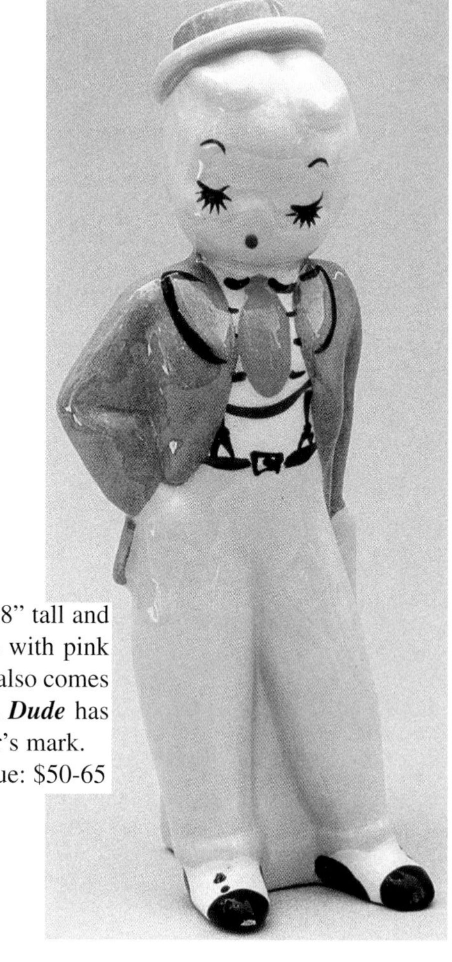

**(54)** ***Dude*** is 8" tall and is shown here with pink tone skin. He also comes in white. This ***Dude*** has the 'E' painter's mark.
Estimated value: $50-65

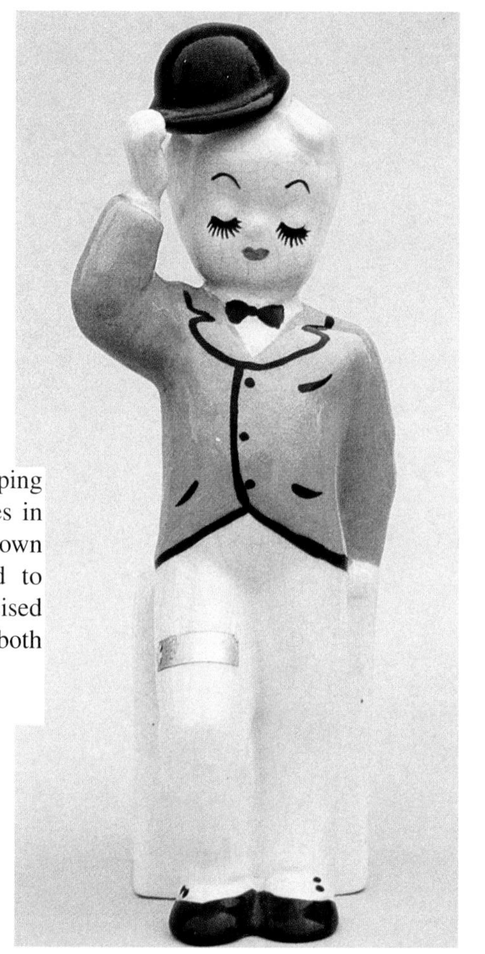

**(55)** ***Danny*** is 9" tall and tipping his gentlemanly hat. He comes in white and pink skin tones as shown here. ***Danny*** is also painted to match the ladies. They are incised 'deLee Art © 1947'. They both have name labels.
Estimated value: $35-50

**(56)** ***Panchita*** and ***Pedro*** were a very popular pair and were made for many years. They come in a wide assortment of painting treatments. We have never seen either one with open eyes. ***Panchita*** is 7" tall and has a planter in her skirt. She is incised 'deLee Art © LA, 44'.
Estimated value for
Panchita: $30-45

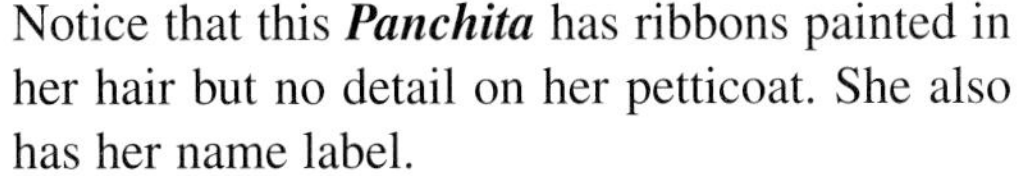
Notice that this ***Panchita*** has ribbons painted in her hair but no detail on her petticoat. She also has her name label.

They make a darling couple. This pair was painted to match.

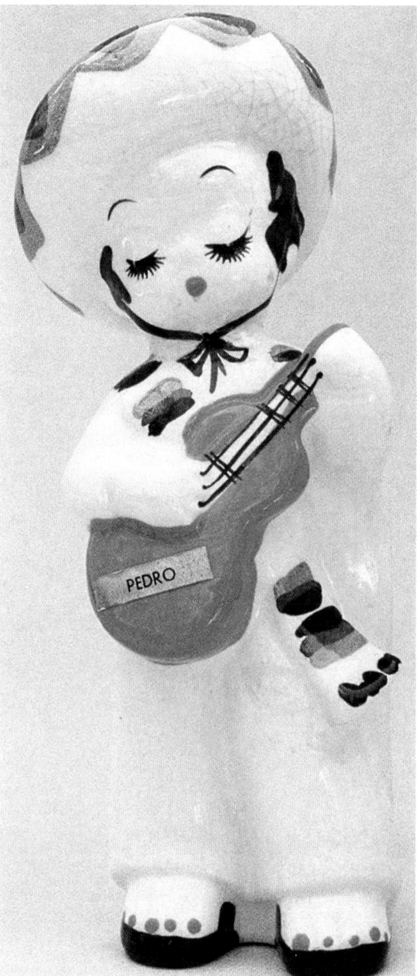


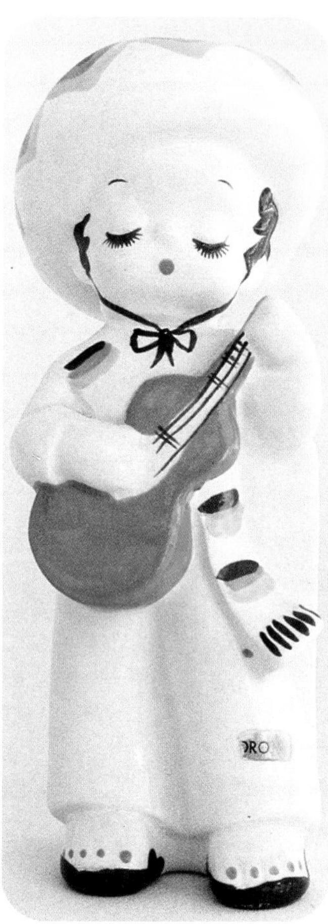

**(57)** ***Pedro*** is a handsome fellow, strumming away on his guitar. He is 8" tall and is incised 'deLee Art, Hollywood, USA, 44'. He has the 'E' painter's mark. His planter is behind him. Estimated value: $30-45

Two more examples of colorful combinations for this pair.

**(58 and 59)** A pleasing Chinese pair. ***Oh Boy*** is 8½" tall and is incised '© deLee Art Co., 1948, Hollywood'. ***Oh Joy*** is 8" tall and is incised 'deLee Art 1947 ©'. They are both planters. The expensive 14 carat gold paint was applied after the glost firing and then fired again. True to Chinese mode, the boy wears a skirt and the girl, pants.
Estimated value for the pair: $100-125

Two more examples of different painting schemes. Above is ***Oh Boy*** and below ***Oh Joy***.

Here you see the front and back of a differently painted ***Oh Boy***.

**(60 and 61)** A different Oriental pair, ***Sing*** and ***Song***. ***Sing*** is the boy on the left and ***Song***, the girl on the right. They are 9" tall and are incised '1948, deLee Art'.
Estimated value for the pair: $100-125

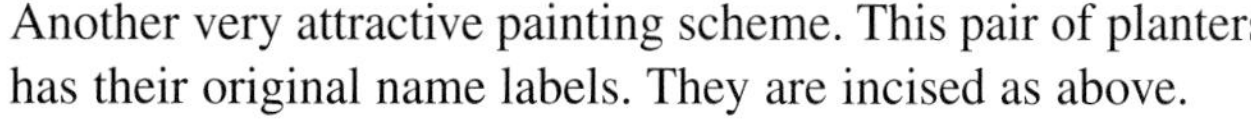
Another very attractive painting scheme. This pair of planters has their original name labels. They are incised as above.

**(62 and 63)** This Dutch couple (above) was very popular and so many examples are found today. ***Katrina*** is 6½" tall and ***Hans*** is 7" tall. They came in white and pink toned skin. ***Katrina*** is marked 'delee Art, Hollywood, 1944'. ***Hans's*** mark is blurred. They both have their name labels. This pair also comes with dark brown pants and scarf for ***Hans*** and brown matching trim for ***Katrina***.
Estimated value for the pair: $70-90

This pink toned pair are incised 'deLee Art, Hollywood, LA'. They have both their round deLee labels and their name labels.

**(64)** This figure, appropriately named ***Angel***, is 6½" and is incised 'deLee Art, 1944', with an 'E' painter's mark. She has little wings in back as shown.
Estimated value: $35-50

**(65, 66 and 67)** A darling trio of heavenly angels. They are 4½". From left to right, ***Joy***, incised 'deLee Art, USA ©'; ***Star***, with candle holder incised 'deLee Art'; and ***Carol***, incised 'deLee Art'.
Estmated value each: $25-35

**(68 and 69)** Four different painting versions of a precious angelic pair. They are ***Twinkle*** and ***Star***. They are 4½-5" tall and were modeled to each hold a birthday candle as shown below. Estimated value each: $25-35

This pair (above) comes from the older production because of the more simple painting style. The pair on the right are pink toned models.

**(70)** This angel is 6½" tall, is not incised and has no markings.
Estimated value: $40-60

**(71)** Madonna and child, ***Ava Maria***, is 6" tall. She has a deLee sticker and her name label.
Estimated value: $50-75

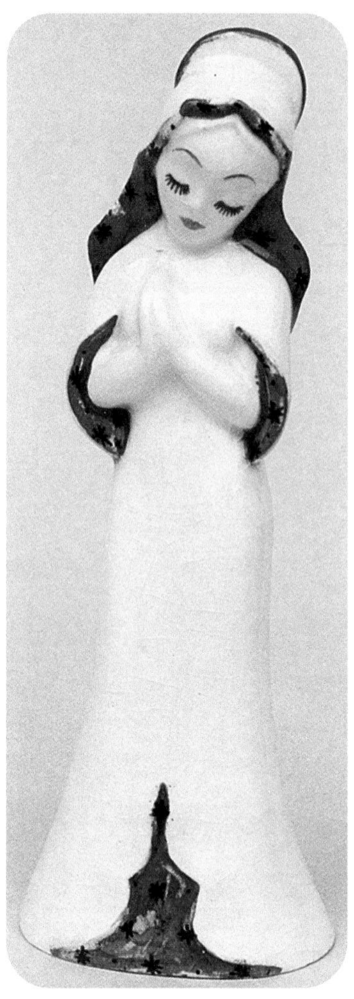

**(72)** This beautiful Madonna, ***Dolores***, is 8" tall and is incised 'Dolores © 39 deLee Art, USA'.
Estimated value: $75-100

**(73)** The deLee ***Nativity*** set is very rare. This set is owned by a family member. There were some sets produced but no one remembers how many. This set is missing the donkey. The prototype figures are shown on page 29.
Estimated value: $250-300

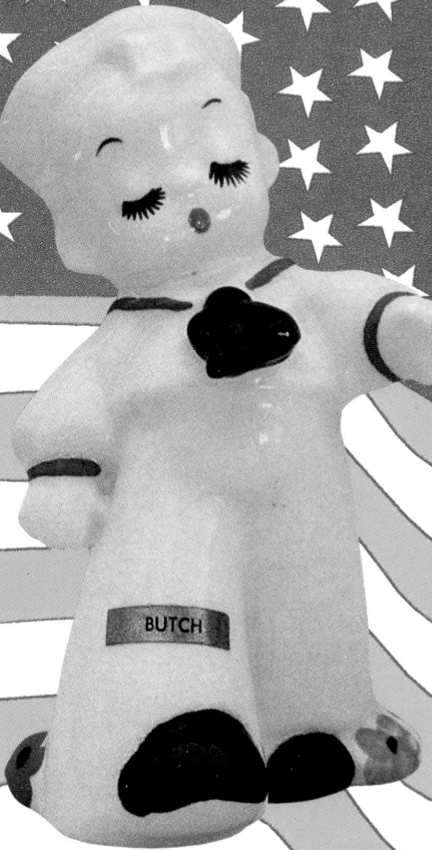

**(75) Delightful 6" *Yard Bird* with his wide open eyes and little gun. He has a deLee label and his name label. He comes painted in two different shades of brown, lighter and darker.**
**Estimated value: $40-60**

**(74) This set of figures is particularly engaging in their WW II outfits. *Butch* is a 6" sailor with tie flying! He is incised 'deLee Art 1942'. He has deLee and name labels.**
**Estimated value: $40-60**

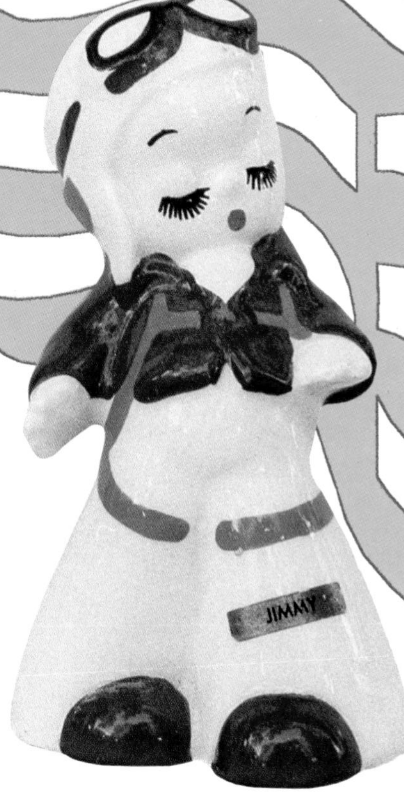

**(76) *Jimmie*** is 6½" tall and is an aviator. Some collectors refer to this figure as Amelia Earhart, but he was modeled to be a boy. Jimmie Lee does not remember intentionally naming this figure after herself. It just seemed an appropriate name at the time. He is the most difficult of the three to find.
Estimated value: $50-70

On the left is a side view of ***Butch*** showing his tie flying. On the right is the lighter tan version of ***Yard Bird's*** uniform. Below is ***Jimmie's*** back side showing the parachute pack detail.

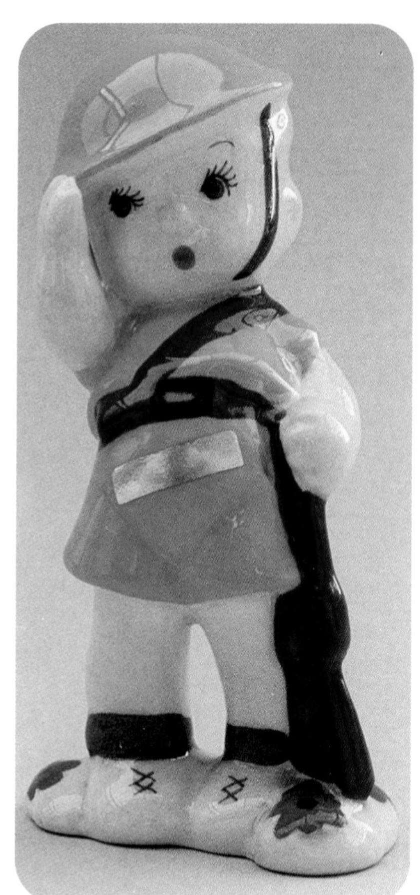

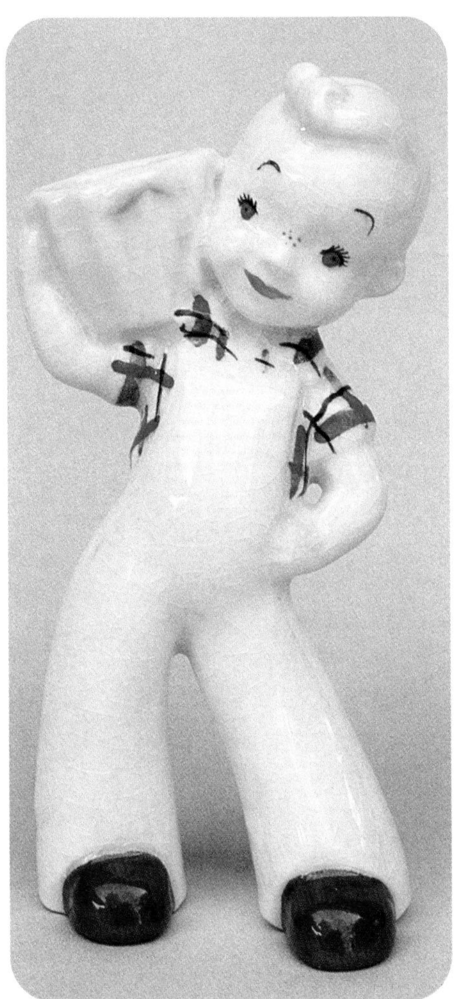

**(78)** ***Sis*** is 6¾" tall and is believed to be a pair with Buddy. She holds a jar in her hands that forms a planter. She comes in combinations of blue and green colors and possibly others yet unseen by us.
Estimated value for ***Sis***: $45-60

**(77)** ***Buddy*** is 7" tall and is carrying a basket on his shoulder. His basket forms the planter. He does not have any labels and is not incised. He is found with open eyes only.
Estimated value for ***Buddy***: $45-60

**(79)** ***Mary*** is 6½" tall with her lamb molded to her side. She is incised 'deLee Art 1938', and '***Mary***' in cursive on the bottom. She is painted in the early style. She is holding a vase which is her planter. She has the deLee label.
Estimated value: $50-65

**(80)** ***Miss Muffet*** is 5" high. She looks startled as the spider comes up from the mushroom and over her skirt. The scene is complete with the porridge bowl. She has her name label. This figure also comes with 12 holes (¼") in the back to be used as a flower frog.
Estimated value: $90-125

***Jack Be Nimble***, a little boy with a candlestick, was also made but none have been found to photograph. There are others in this nursery rhyme series as well.

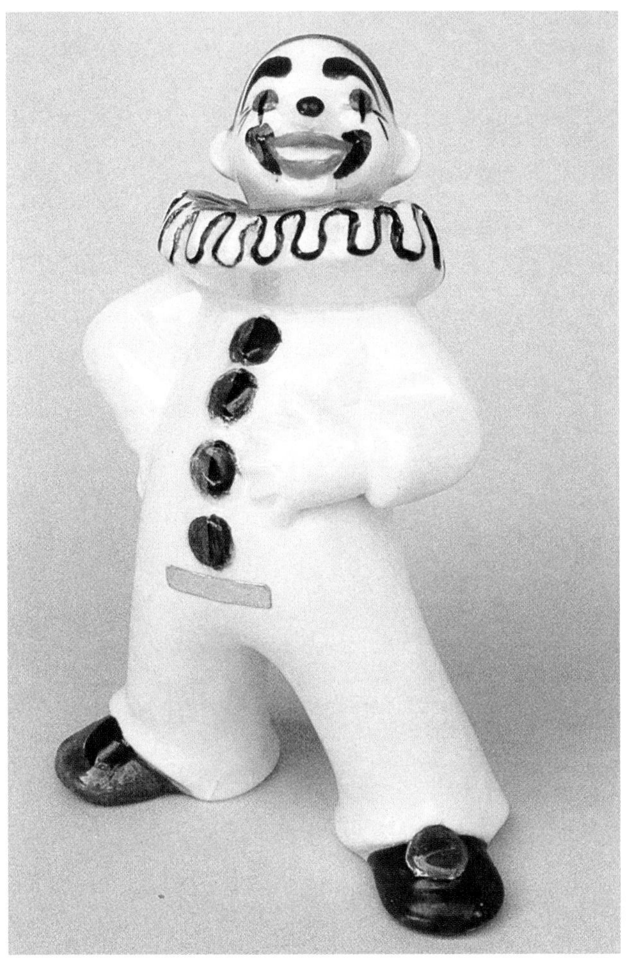

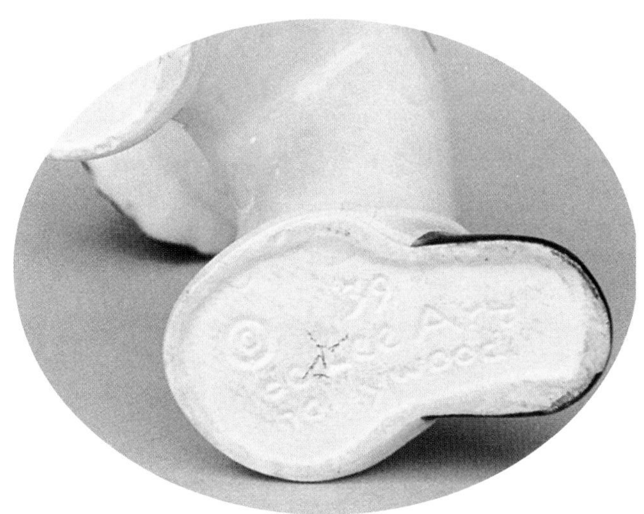

**(81)** ***Joey*** is a handsome 7½" clown with a definite presence. He is incised 'deLee Art 1939'. He is a rare figure.
Estimated value: $110-150

**(82)** In the early 1940's, Jimmie Lee licensed the rights to produce a few of the Walter Lantz cartoon characters. This is ***8 Ball*** from the cartoon of the same name. He is 4½" tall. He is incised 'deLee Art © 40 USA, A Walter Lantz Creation'.
Estimated value: $75-100

**(83)** These are 2 of 3 poses produced of ***Andy Pandy***. They are incised 'deLee Art © 40, A Walter Lantz Creation'. They also have round deLee labels on their bases.
Estimated value for each: $75-100

***Woody Woodpecker*** was also produced but none have been found to photograph.

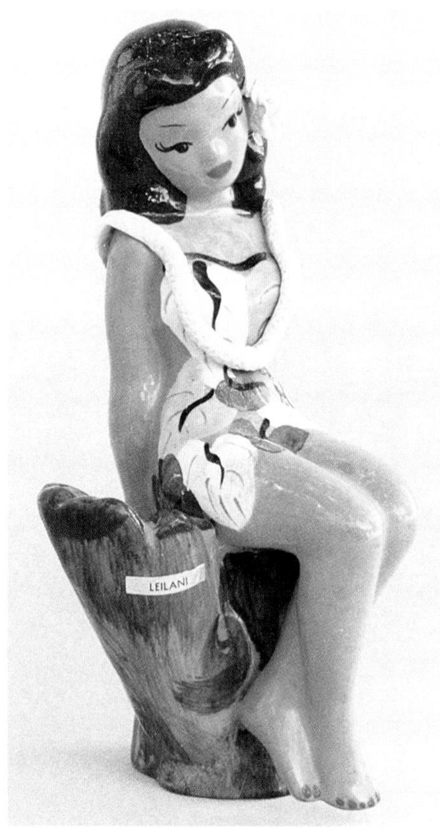


**(84)** Seated ***Leilani*** is 9" high. She has a lovely tanned Hawaiian skin and is wearing a one-piece bathing suit with an applied lei. She has her name label.
Estimated value: $150-175

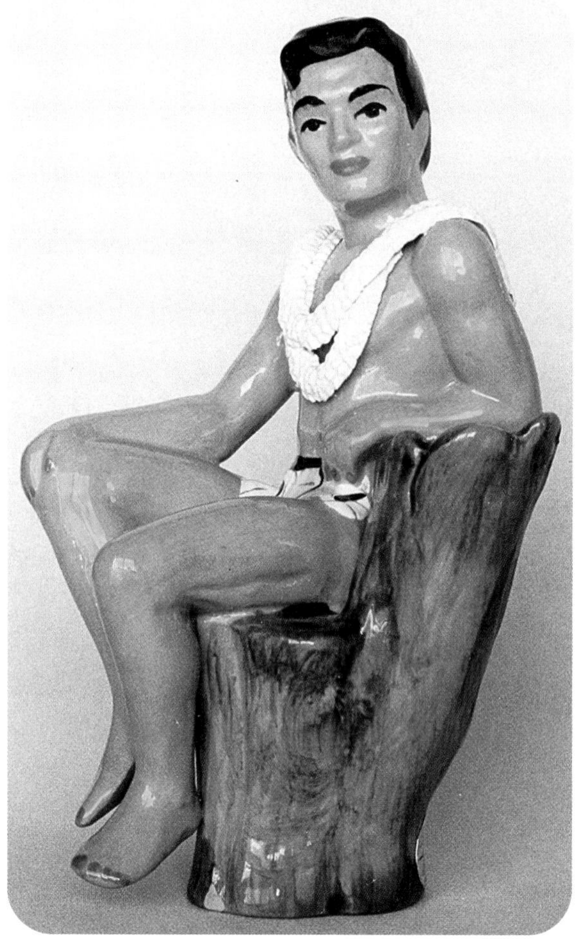

**(85)** Seated ***Maui*** is 9" high. He has an Hawaiian tan and two applied leis.
Estimated value: $150-175

**(86)** Standing ***Leilani*** is 11" tall. She has a two-piece bathing suit. There is also a standing ***Maui***. These figures have been seen as bases for commercially made lamps. An order from a lamp company was filled for this purpose.
Estimated value: $160-225

**(87)** 14" ***Can-Can Dancer*** is clearly a figure from the 1950's as she has the incised round mark of that time. She comes in several different color combinations and has the 'E' painter mark.
Estimated value: $150-175

**(88 and 89)** Here we have ***Pedro*** and ***Panchita*** grown up! ***Pedro*** switched from Guitar to drums and ***Panchita*** is dancing more. ***Panchita*** is 13" and the kneeling ***Pedro*** is 7½". She has many touches of 24 carat gold paint which is applied after the glost firing and then refired. Her mold is very complicated with arms and leg away from her body. She has a deLee sticker and a 'P' painter's mark. He is incised 'deLee Art' with an 'E' painters mark and a ***Pedro*** name label.
Estimated value for the pair: $225-300

(**90** and **91**) This pair of Latino dancers are 11½" and 13" tall respectively. They are very exotic in modeling and mood. There is an interesting use of the gold paint as well.

Jimmie Lee was surprised when shown this pair as she did not remember modeling figures with so much daring and decolletage. They are incised 'deLee Art USA'.
Estimated value for the pair: $225-300

(**92** and **93**) A pair of Siamese Dancers that are 13" tall. The gold paint is used mostly for their jewelry. They are incised 'deLee Art ©'and are very gracefully modeled. They also come in all white clothes with gold trim.
Estimated value for the pair: $225-300

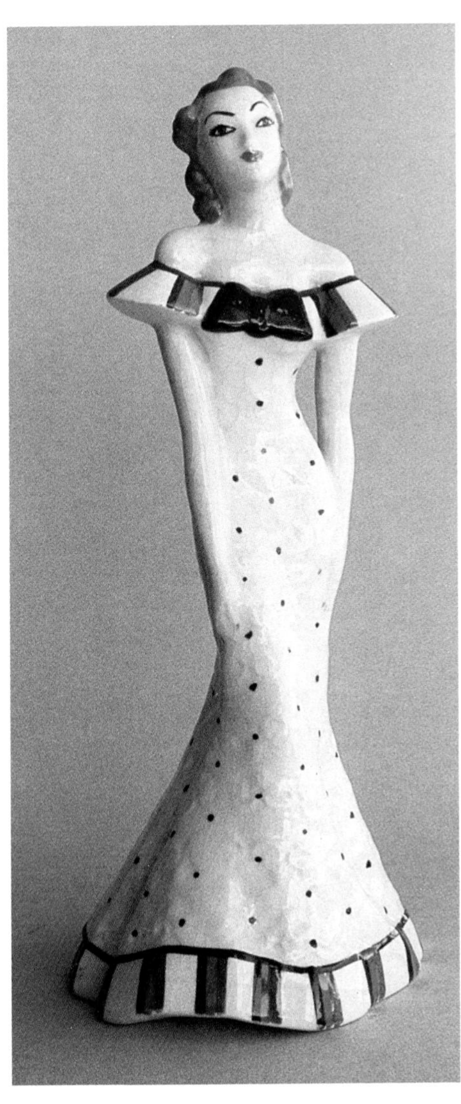

**(94)** A lovely 9" tall art deco lady in her gown. Both of the facing figures are from the same mold but painted very differently, especially in the facial features.

Note the early deLee sticker on the right-hand figure indicating these were made in the early 1940's.
Estimated value: $100-150

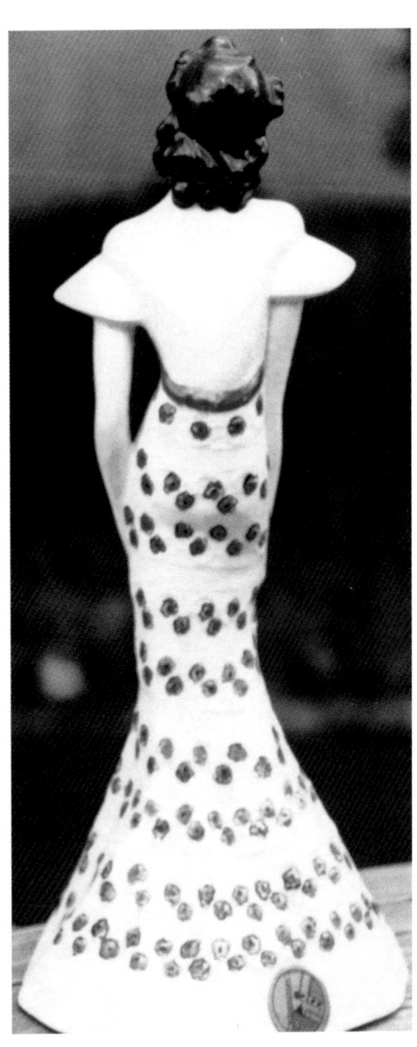

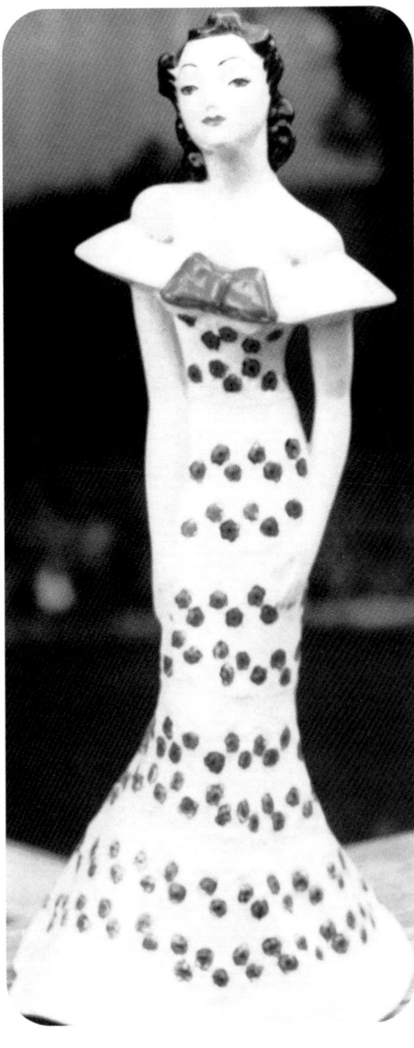

**(95)** ***Maria Candelaria*** is 10½". She is graceful balancing a large basket of fruit on her head. She is incised 'deLee Art Hollywood © 1943 Calif. USA' and has a deLee sticker.
Estimated value: $90-125

(255) ***Lorenzo*** is 10½". He is paired with ***Maria*** and carries a large bowl of flowers on his head. He has his name tag and deLee sticker.
Estimated value: $90-125

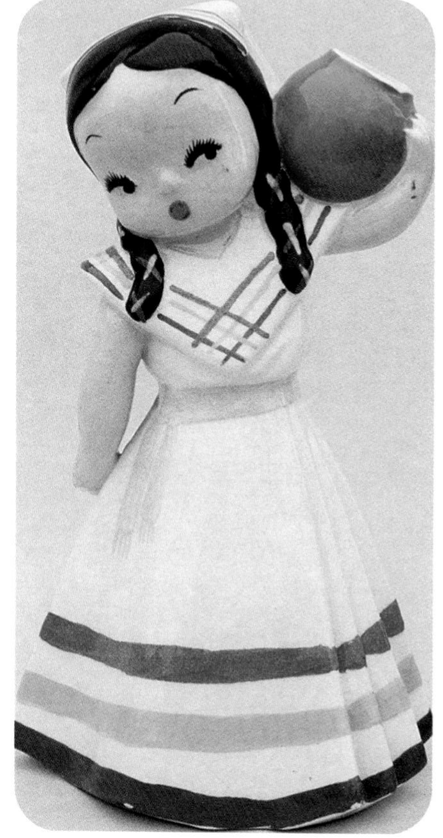

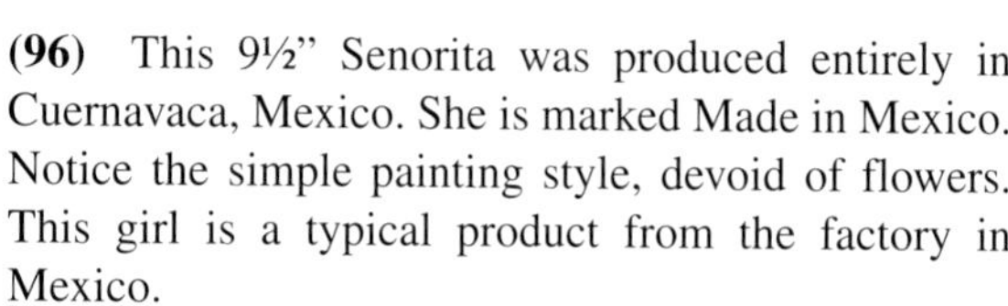

**(96)** This 9½" Senorita was produced entirely in Cuernavaca, Mexico. She is marked Made in Mexico. Notice the simple painting style, devoid of flowers. This girl is a typical product from the factory in Mexico.
Estimated value: $35-50

**(97)** This charming 10" girl, ***Annie***, is carrying a well defined basket that is a planter. She is inscised 'deLee Art 1940 © Hollywood'.
Estimated value: $65-85

**(98)** Another charmer below is 9½" tall. She has a planter in back and the painting style of the early figures. She does not have any stickers and is not incised. Her back view is shown below left.
Estimated value: $65-85

**(99)** This little 4" Cocker Spaniel, ***Smoothie***, is seen more often than most of the other dogs. His painting varies from very light to medium tan. This one is incised 'deLee Art © 41 USA' and has his name plate.
Estimated value: $25-35

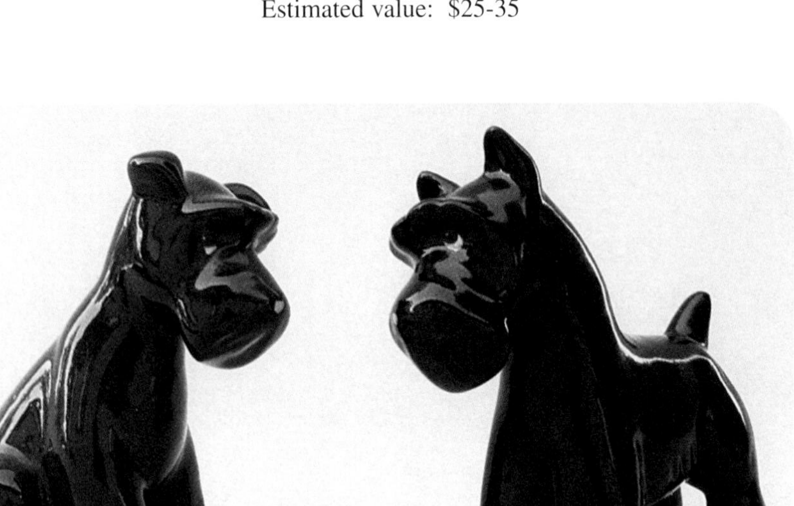

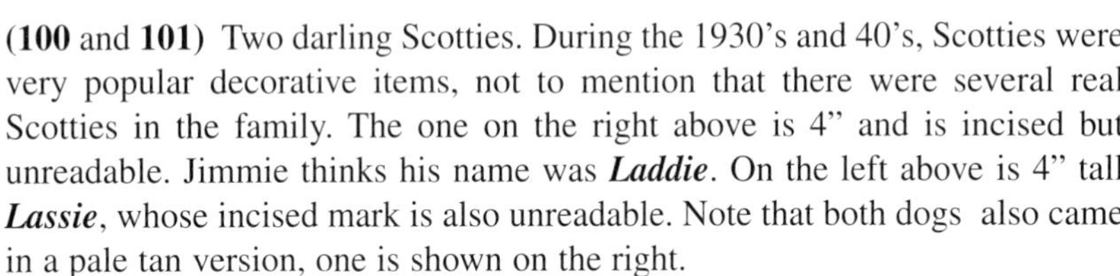

**(100** and **101)** Two darling Scotties. During the 1930's and 40's, Scotties were very popular decorative items, not to mention that there were several real Scotties in the family. The one on the right above is 4" and is incised but unreadable. Jimmie thinks his name was ***Laddie***. On the left above is 4" tall ***Lassie***, whose incised mark is also unreadable. Note that both dogs also came in a pale tan version, one is shown on the right.
Estimated value each: $35-50

**(102** and **103)** This pair, 2½ and 3" tall, are a good example of deLee's later figurines. They were probably made during the 1950's using the airbrushing technique, with details done with a brush. They have the ½" sticker and a 'P' painters mark.
Estimated value each: $35-45

**(104)** A cute 5" poodle with a flower has no stickers or incising but is definitely deLee.
Estimated value: $35-50

**(105)** ***Rags*** is a perfect name for this 4" English Sheepdog. His eyes are completely obscured by hair. He is not marked but sports his name plate.
Estimated value: $35-45

**(106)** A very different poodle from deLee. The hair is like "tiny spaghetti", painted with silver, and he has a silver collar. In this pose, he is 6½" tall and is marked with the 1950's deLee stamp. He also comes in black with silver paint.
Estimated value: $70-90

**(107)** This is an extremely rare piece. The poodle is 3½" high and has no label or name plate. We know it is deLee because it is owned by a family member.
Estimated value: $135-160

**(108)** ***Schnitz*** is a 6" long Dachshund and has a deLee sticker and his name plate. Note the open eyes.
Estimated value: $45-60

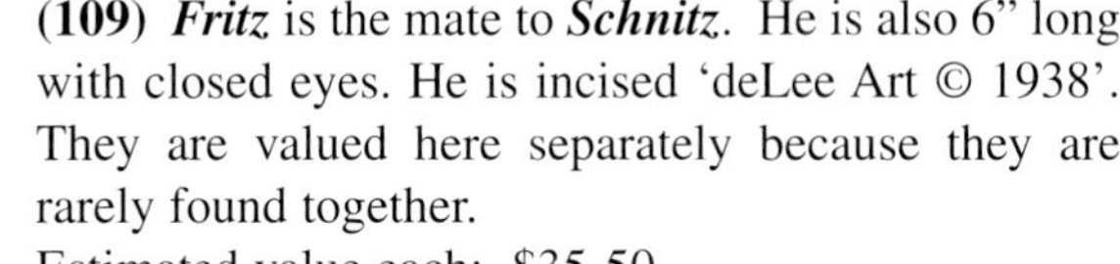

**(109)** ***Fritz*** is the mate to ***Schnitz***. He is also 6" long with closed eyes. He is incised 'deLee Art © 1938'. They are valued here separately because they are rarely found together.
Estimated value each: $35-50

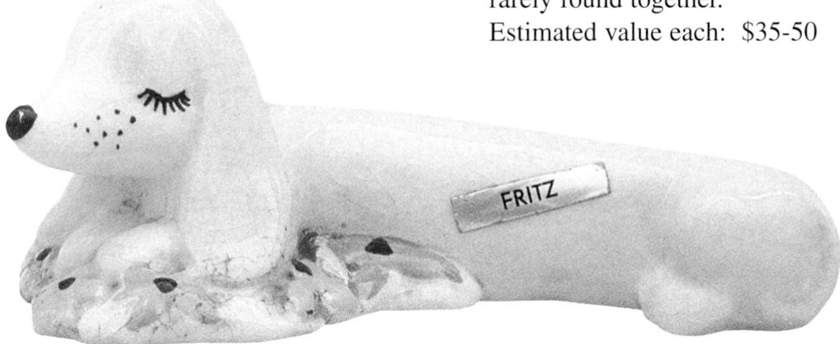


**(110** and **111)** A cute pair of Airedales, 3¾" tall. The one on the right is ***Sandy***. We do not know the name for the one on the left.
Estimated value for the pair:
$75-100

**(112)** ***Mickey*** is 4" tall and is very animated playing with his ball. The ball is found painted many different ways.
Estimated value: $45-60

**(113)** This coy little cat named ***Kitty*** is 4" tall with flowers painted on her leg. She is not incised but has her name plate.
Estimated value: $35-45

**(114)** A wide eyed cat ready for play. He is 4½" tall and is incised '© 41 deLee Art LA, USA'.
Estimated value: $35-45

**(115** and **116)** A cute pair of cats, painted to match. ***Puss***, 3½", is on the left, lying down. The seated cat on the right is probably named ***Boots*** (name not seen, however). He is incised 'deLee Art © 1948 CAL' and is 4" tall. Estimated value for each: $30-40

**(117, 118** and **119)** This group of Siamese cats are three examples from 12 molds purchased by Jimmie Lee from another artist. The cat at left is 8" tall, is airbrushed and has a deLee sticked on his back.

The pair below are 8" long, airbrushed and have deLee stickers. Estimated value for each: $25-30

These are more cats from the purchased molds. They are all beautifully airbrushed, probably made in the 1950's.

**(120** and **121)** The cat on the left is 3" long, the one on the right is 3½" tall. They both have the ½" deLee stickers.
Estimated value each: $20-35

**(122)** This cat is 5" tall and has the deLee label.
Estimated value: $35-45

**(123)** This graceful cat lying down is 6" high at the head. The eyes are beautifully painted.
Estimated value: $75-100

**(124)** An elegant 12" tall Siamese. She is incised 'deLee Art ©', is airbrushed and also has beautiful eyes.
Estimated value: $75-125

(125) This little rabbit has a cleverly concealed planter in her hat. She is 7" tall and sports a deLee sticker on her back. The big, blue eyes add to her charm.
Estimated value: $50-65

**(126)** ***Peter*** is 5" tall with a lovely bouquet. He is incised 'deLee Art, 1939.'
Estimated value: $35-50

**(127 and 128)** ***Hopalong*** and ***Cottontail*** are a darling pair of pink bunnies. They have ½" deLee stickers and are about 5" tall.
Estimated value for the pair: $60-75

Another pair of pink bunnies. On the left is ***Honey Bun*** and the right is ***Bunny Hug***. They are 3½" and 5½" tall. Estimated value for the pair: $60-75

**(129)** A white version of ***Bunny Hug***. She has a name plate but no other markings.
Estimated value: $30-35

**(130)** ***Honey Bun*** with a surprise. The tail area is cut out so that you can put cotton for a tail. She really isn't big enough to be a cotton dispenser, it's more for fun. She has a deLee sticker on the bottom.
Estimated value: $30-35

A matching pair of ***Bunny Hug*** and ***Honey Bun***.
Estimated value for the pair: $60-70

**(131)** ***Hopalong*** bunny planter. He is 6" tall, and is unusual with the wide open eyes. Note the ***Hopalong*** below with closed eyes. He has a deLee sticker on his back and is incised 'deLee Art © 1941 LA USA'.
Estimated value: $35-45

This is an unusual ***Hopalong*** as his head is more turned to the right than the others. It was probably turned slightly while it was green ware. Notice the yellow wash and closed eyes. He is incised 'deLee Art 1941'.
Estimated value: $35-45

**(132)** This is yet another version of ***Hopalong*** (also found with the name ***Cottontail***) but his head is tilted to the left, not right. He also has an Easter egg planter instead of a basket. Also note the open eyes.
Estimated value: $35-45

This ***Hopalong*** (left) illustrates the deep modeling and sharp lines of a figurine that has come from a "new mold". The molds are poured about 100 times. The first ones are much more defined than the later ones. The mold erodes a tiny bit with each pouring.

**(133)** ***Bunny*** is 5" tall and has a different mouth painting style.
Estimated value: $40-50

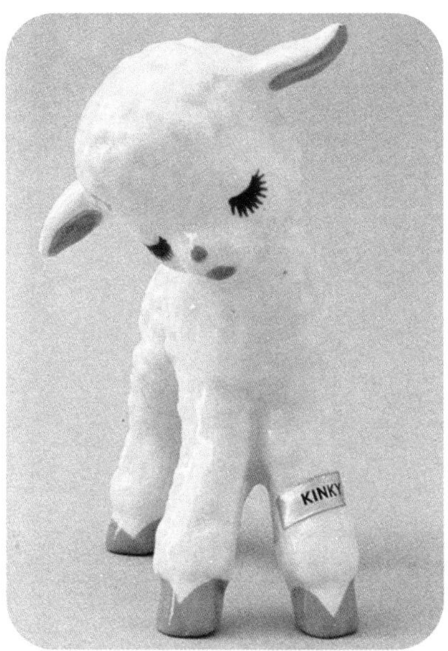


**(134)** ***Kinky***
Estimated value: $25-35

This little pair of lambs are ***Kinky*** and ***Curly***. ***Kinky*** is standing and is 5" tall. He has his name plate. ***Curly*** is 3" high and lying down. He has no marks or stickers. Estimated value for the pair: $50-70

**(135)** ***Curly***
Estimated value: $25-35

**(136)** This lamb was created to meet the demand of a larger vase. He is 8" tall and has no markings. Estimated value: $45-60

**(145 and 146)** It appears that there are several different lambs in this group but actually it's the same mold for all of them. On top left is 4" tall ***Whitey*** and right is ***Blackie***. ***Whitey*** and ***Blackie*** also came as planters, shown here on the left, also. Posing them and photographing them at different angles makes them appear to be different molds.
Estimated value for ***Whitey***: $30-40
Estimated value for ***Blackie***: $50-70

**(147)** This little lamb's name is unknown to us. He is 3¾" tall.His front legs are on the base and his back legs are kicking free. His ears are flying! He is marked '© deLee Art 1943'.
Estimated Value: $45-60

(**141** and **142**) ***Cuddles*** and ***Bubbles***, both of whom are 3" tall, make a cute pair with open and closed eyes. ***Bubbles*** does not have any markings except his name label. ***Cuddles*** has no markings
Estimated value for each: $25-35

**(143)** This fellow is 5" tall with a great blue bow. He has no markings or name label.
Estimated value: $35-45

**(144)** This is a very small lamb at 2" tall. He has the deLee Mexico sticker which reads, 'DELEE ART CO. Cuernavaca MEXICO'. He is a very appealing little guy.
Estimated value: $60-75

Here is ***Tom*** as a planter. He is also painted with some flowers. He has no stickers or markings. Estimated value: $20-35

**(137 and 138)** This cute pair is ***Tom*** and ***Jerry***. They are 4" tall and neither one is a planter.***Tom*** has a deLee sticker on his leg and is incised 'deLee Art'. ***Jerry*** has a deLee sticker but is not incised. Estimated value for the pair: $45-60

**(139 and 140)** A pair of young donkeys, ***Rock*** and ***Rye*** are 3" tall. ***Rye*** is on the left, and ***Rock*** on the right. ***Rock*** is carefully balanced on his small base. Both donkeys have their deLee stickers. There is some disagreement as to the species of these guys. We chose donkey, others say they're lambs. Estimated value for the pair: $60-75

**(148)** This elegant draft horse is 8½" tall. His planter opening is formed by his mane. He does not have any markings or labels.
Estimated value: $50-75

**(149)** ***Amigo*** is a 5" tall donkey and is incised '© CA '39 deLee Art'. He is appealing with his freckles. Notice his open eyes.
Estimated value: $50-60

**(150 and 151)** A pair of horses with action modeled into their design. Above left is ***Nip***. He is 5" tall. The horse above is 3" tall. We do not know his name but suspect that it is ***Tuck***, as in nip and tuck. Jimmie Lee named many pairs in this fashion.
Estimated value for the pair: $80-100

**(152)** A very different 3" by 3" horse. He has a deLee label. His painting is very abstract.
Estimated value: $40-60

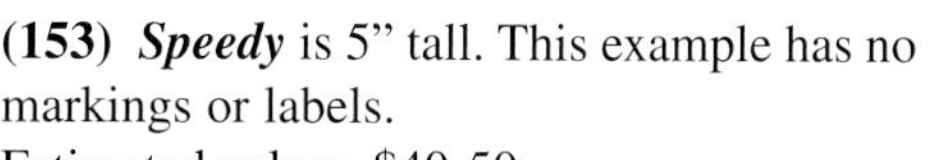

**(153)** ***Speedy*** is 5" tall. This example has no markings or labels.
Estimated value: $40-50

**(154)** A happy fellow who just won the big race. His flower wreath is separate and applied. He is 5" tall and has no markings or labels.
Estimated value: $60-75

**(155)** This horse has been photographed from both the right and left sides. It's fun to see the movement that Jimmie Lee expertly modeled into these figurines. You can really imagine him running. He is 4" tall and has no markings or labels.
Estimated value: $45-55

**(156 and 157)** Here we have ***Sadie*** and ***Cy***. Does poor old ***Cy*** look hen-pecked or what? ***Sadie*** has a clearly superior attitude. ***Cy*** can do anything he wants as long as ***Sadie*** approves. She is 3" tall and he is 2½" tall. They both have deLee stickers and name labels.
Estimated value for the pair: $60-75

**(158 and 159)** Two of the best loved deLee animals. ***Grunt*** and ***Groan*** are more commonly found today because more were made originally due to their popularity. They are very appealing. ***Grunt*** is seated and ***Groan*** is standing. ***Grunt*** is incised 'deLee Art © '42 USA'. All of them have deLee stickers.
Estimated value for the pair: $75-100

**(162)** This little calf is 4" tall and is incised 'deLee Art © 1938'. This group was made as a set of three but not necessarily sold together. He's a very happy fellow.
Estimated value: $35-50

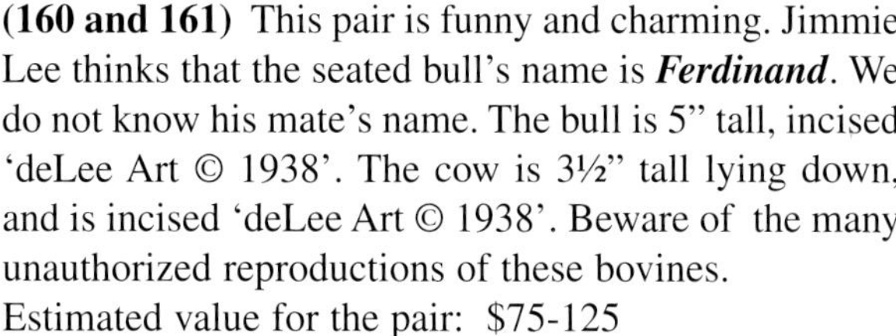

**(160 and 161)** This pair is funny and charming. Jimmie Lee thinks that the seated bull's name is ***Ferdinand***. We do not know his mate's name. The bull is 5" tall, incised 'deLee Art © 1938'. The cow is 3½" tall lying down, and is incised 'deLee Art © 1938'. Beware of the many unauthorized reproductions of these bovines.
Estimated value for the pair: $75-125

This pair is even funnier from the rear view.

**(163)** ***Chesty*** is 3½" tall and is incised 'deLee Art USA'. He also has a deLee sticker on the bottom. Shown here are two different flower painting designs.
Estimated value: $35-45

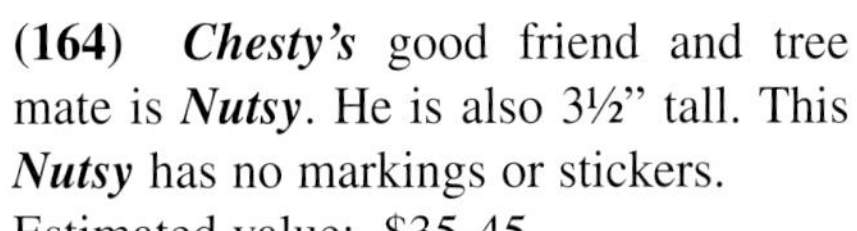

**(164)** ***Chesty's*** good friend and tree mate is ***Nutsy***. He is also 3½" tall. This ***Nutsy*** has no markings or stickers.
Estimated value: $35-45

**(165)** Chipmunks are also a part of the deLee family. This is ***Mrs. Chips***, complete with her nut gathering basket. She is 4¼" tall and incised 'deLee Art 40 USA'. Notice the difference in painting technique between her and the one below. Estimated value: $25-35

**(166)** ***Mr. Chips*** is 4½" tall and is incised 'deLee Art 1940'. His planter is formed by an acorn. Estimated value: $25-35

***Mr. and Mrs. Chips*** with slightly different painting versions. Her basket and his acorn are planter/vases.

***Stinkie*** 4¼", and ***Phew*** 4½" at his tail tip.

A rear view of ***Stinkie*** showing his early (1937-1944) label.

The ever popular, best selling, skunks! It's amazing to see how expressive the eyes are, just using black and white. The different ways that their eyes are painted changes their expressions completely. This page shows different views of ***Stinkie, Phew*** and ***Squirt***. These fellows are among the easiest deLee figurines to find because so many of them were made.
Estimated value each: $15-25

***Stinkie*** and ***Squirt***, 3½" from a different angle.

***(167, 168 and 169) Phew, Stinkie*** and ***Squirt***

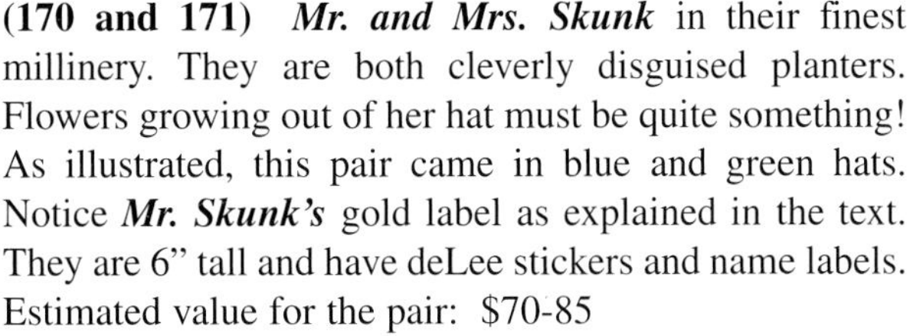
**(170 and 171)** ***Mr. and Mrs. Skunk*** in their finest millinery. They are both cleverly disguised planters. Flowers growing out of her hat must be quite something! As illustrated, this pair came in blue and green hats. Notice ***Mr. Skunk's*** gold label as explained in the text. They are 6" tall and have deLee stickers and name labels. Estimated value for the pair: $70-85

**(172)** ***Skunkie*** is 4½" and is incised 'deLee Art 41 USA'. He has a planter in a basket behind him. He has a deLee sticker on his tail.
Estimated value: $40-55

**(173)** ***Woods Pussy*** is 5" tall and has a planter in his bowl. He is incised 'deLee Art 1941'.
Estimated value: $35-50

**(174)** 5" ***Super Stinker*** is a clever takeoff on the 1940's Superman popularity. He comes complete with his paper label that reads: "Why be just disagreeable when with a little more effort you can be a Super Stinker." On the back is the address of deLee Art Co. His large S is not just painted on, it's embossed into the clay.
Estimated value: $30-40 (with tag, $50-65)

**(175)** This fellow is a 6" planter with no labels or incising. It is asssumed that there is probably a mate for this guy.
Estimated value: $30-40

**(177)**

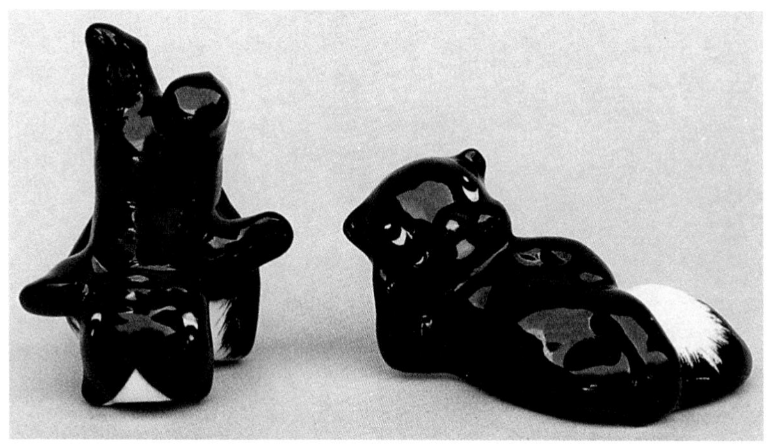

**(178 and 179)** This is a group of very small playful skunks. They are 2¼" to 3½" long. We have found six but there could be more of them.
Estimated value each: $20-35

**(176)** This skunk is the same mold as ***Mr. Skunk*** with a different hat. This guy is sporting a Shriner's fez, obviously a special order from a Shriner's temple. Notice that the red is applied after firing and is now rubbing off. He is 6" tall.
Estimated value: $50-60

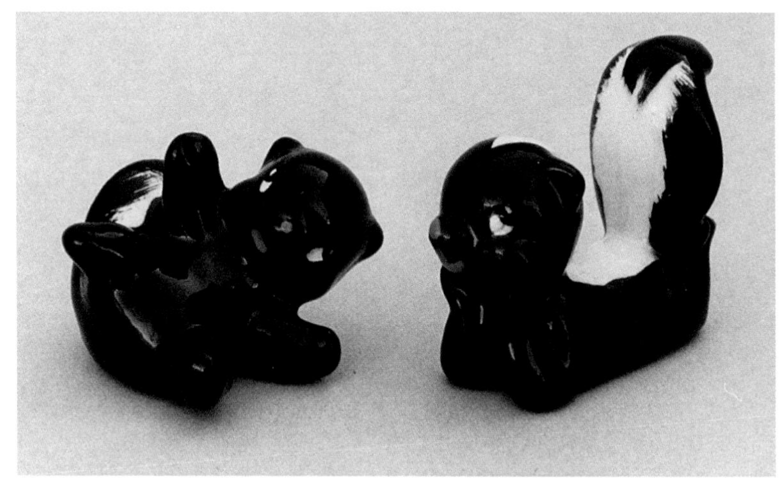

**(180)** **(181)**

**(182)** This is the small 4" Zebra, ***Snookie***. He has a deLee sticker and a name label. Estimated value: $45-60

**(183)** ***Zombie*** is 5" tall with brown stripes. His name label is on his leg. Estimated value: $60-75

**(184)** This fellow is the same mold as ***Zombie*** with black stripes. Interestingly, his name label is ***Zombie Zebra***. Estimated value: $60-75

A different view of ***Zombie***.

**(185)** A cute seal named ***Flipper***. He is 4½" tall and is incised 'deLee Art USA'. He is painted in the early style. Estimated value: $60-75

**(186 and 187)** Would you believe pink elephants! On the left is ***Happy*** and on the right, ***Lucky***. The elephant pair was popular for many years.
Estimated value for the pair: $80-100

The more common white elephants with the early painting style. They are 5" tall. Jimmie Lee always modeled the trunks up as this is a symbol of good luck. Estimated value for the pair: $50-75

Shown here is the back and sideview.

***Lucky*** and ***Happy*** are shown here in the later flower painting style. The trunks are at a slightly different angle for each elephant because they were gently tweaked while in the green ware (unfired clay ware) stage.

**(188)** ***Peanuts*** is a 7" planter, incised 'deLee 1948' and has his name label.
Estimated value: $75-95

**(189)** Two very different painting techniques on the same 5½" bear mold named ***Pee Wee***. The bear on the left has MEXICO printed on the bottom. The bear on the right is incised 'deLee Art 1942 LA ' and also has a deLee sticker on the bottom.
Estimated value each: $45-55

**(190)** Another two bears, very different looking but from the same mold. They are 4" tall. The fellow on the left has no incised markings. The bear on the right has an added hat and was made for the UCLA Bookstore.
Estimated value each: $50-65

**(191)** We do not know this fellow's name. He is 5½" tall and is incised 'deLee Art LA'. He's very appealing in his overalls.
Estimated value: $45-55

**(192)** Clearly this little bear is from the company's work in the 1950's. He is airbrushed and carries the ½" deLee sticker. He is 3" tall.
Estimated value: $30-45

**(193)** This 6" Panda is one that Jimmie Lee modeled not under the Walter Lantz license. ***Pancake*** has quite a different look from ***Andy Pandy***.
Estimated value: $50-65

**(194 and 195)** ***Hi Toots*** and ***Toots*** are a pair of very wily foxes. ***Hi Toots*** above has a slightly different painting combination. ***Hi Toots*** is 5" tall and ***Toots*** is 4" and they each have their name labels.
Estimated value for the pair: $65-80

**(196)** This sweet fawn, ***Babe***, is 4" and is incised 'deLee Art 44 LA'. There is no name label.
Estimated value: $30-45

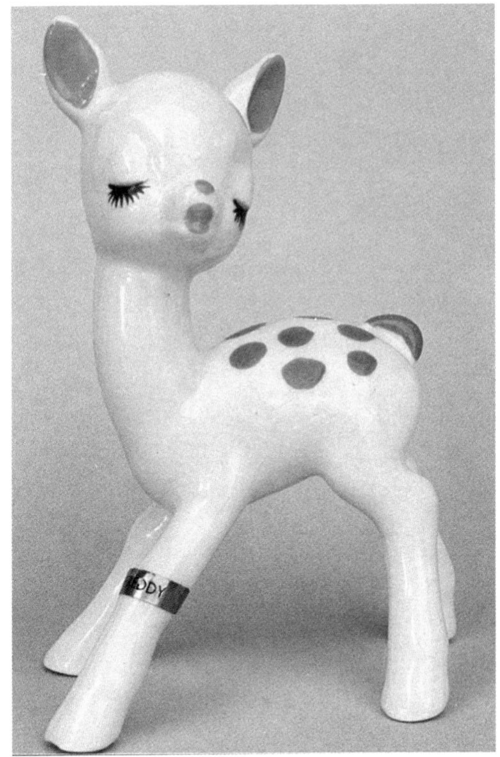

**(197)** 6" ***Freddy*** makes a nice mate for ***Babe*** (left).
Estimated value: $30-45

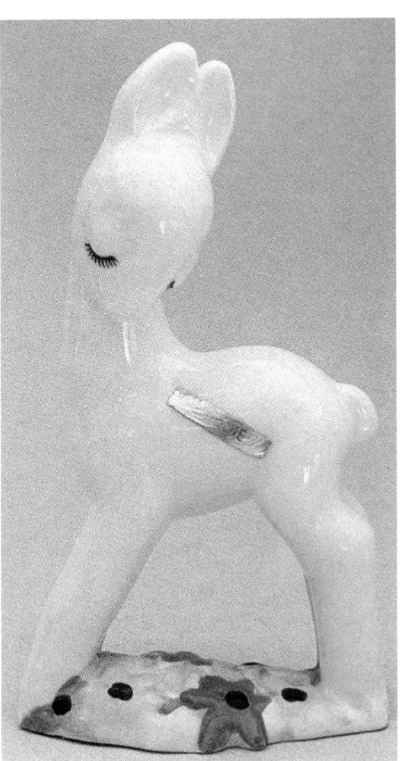

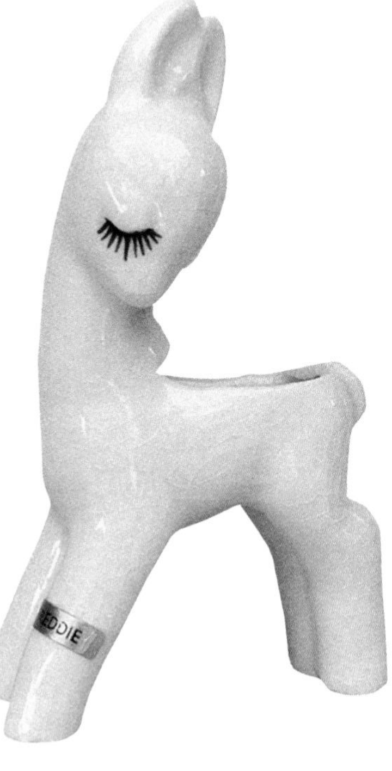

**(198)** This deer, ***Freddie*** (notice the name difference), is shown in two different versions of the same mold. On the left, he is a figurine on a base with flowers. On the right, he is a planter, not on a base. The planter was created by cutting a hole in his back and removing his base while in the green ware stage.
Estimated value: $30-45

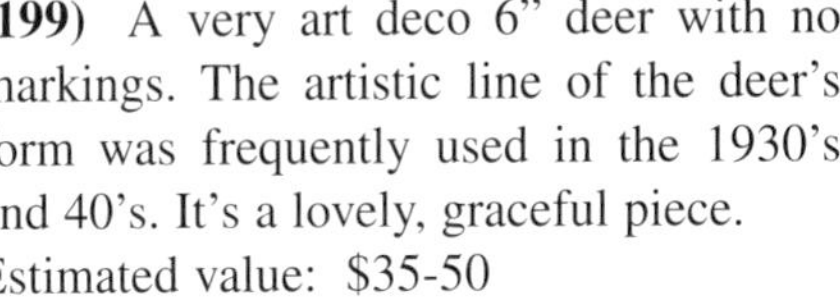

**(199)** A very art deco 6" deer with no markings. The artistic line of the deer's form was frequently used in the 1930's and 40's. It's a lovely, graceful piece.
Estimated value: $35-50

**(200)** ***Tops*** is 6½" tall and is shown here with green or brown patches. Both giraffees have deLee stickers and name labels.
Estimated value for ***Tops***: $50-65

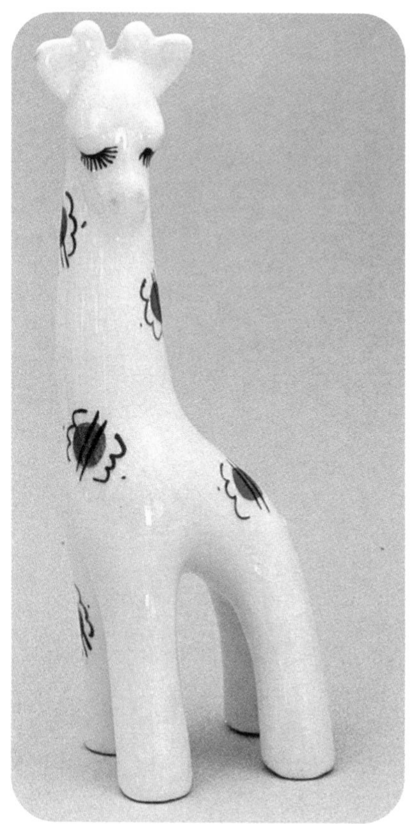

**(202)** The early version of ***Tops*** with the early painting style. This ***Tops*** is 7" tall.
Estimated value: $50-65

**(201)** On the left is ***Topper*** who is the charming mate to ***Tops***. She is slightly smaller and more delicately modeled with her coy closed eyes. ***Tops*** can't take his eyes off of her!
Estimated value for ***Topper***: $50-65

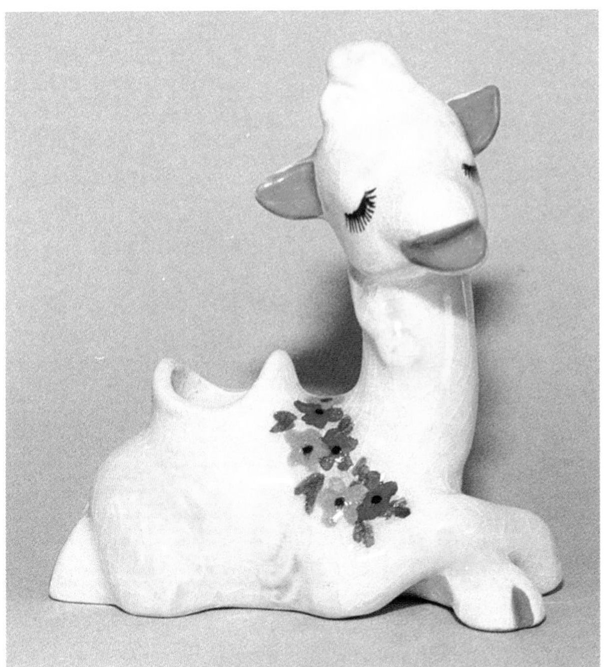

**(203)** ***Sahara Sue*** is one of the author's personal favorites. She is 5" tall and is very humorous with her eyelashes and crossed front legs. She clearly has a presence. Her saddle is the opening of the planter. The one below is a good example of a figurine early out of the mold. Note the sharp contours and well defined molding. This all blurs as the mold is used.
Estimated value: $60-85

**(204)** ***Bimbo*** is 4" tall and has a deLee sticker on his base.
Estimated value: $45-55

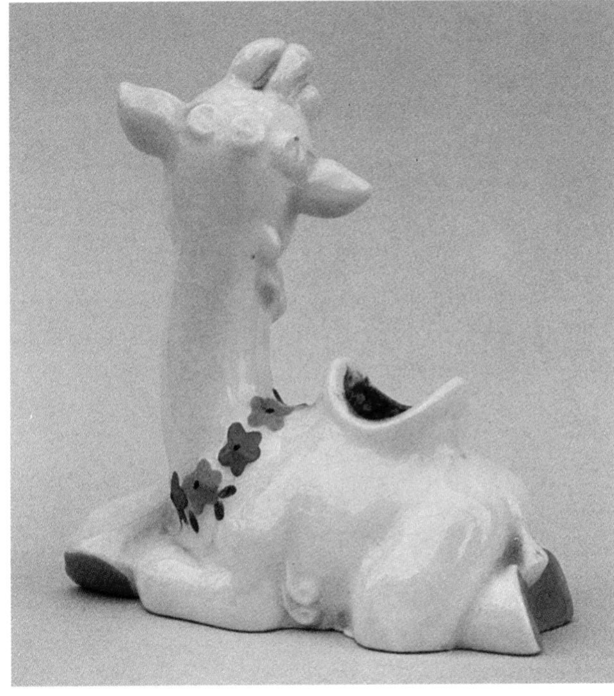

**(205 and 206)** A pair of ducks with the appropriate names of ***Waddle*** and ***Quackie. Waddle*** is very demure and ***Quackie*** is her protector. ***Waddle*** is 4" and ***Quackie*** is 4½". They are both incised 'deLee Art 40 USA'. ***Quackie*** also comes with closed eyes as shown at left. Estimated value for each: $25-35

**(207 and 208)** A fun duck pair, 4½" tall. The duck on the left is ***David*** and above is ***Daniel***. Actually, they are the same mold. ***Daniel's*** duck bill is cut open and spread apart in the green ware stage to create ***David***.
Estimated value for each: $40-50

**(209 and 210)** Our love birds, ***Donna*** and ***Dickie*** are 3½" tall. ***Donna*** has the typical deLee "girl look" with the closed eyes and eyelashes while ***Dickie*** has the wide open "boy" eyes.
Estimated value for the pair: $50-60

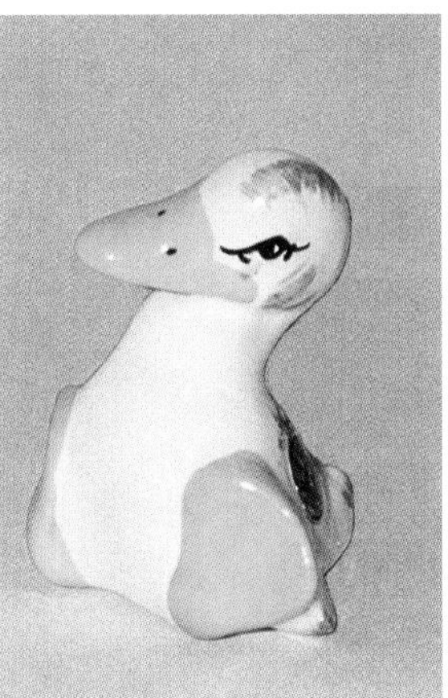

**(211, 212 and 213)** 1950's version of ***Waddles*** and ***Quack*** (no longer ***Quackie***). This group is more realistically painted with airbrushing and finishing by hand. They all have the ½" deLee sticker.
Estimated value each: $25-35

**(214)** ***Butch*** is a rotund piggy bank who is 5" tall. There is a cork underneath that can be removed to collect the coins. There are no incised markings or stickers on this example.
Estimated value: $50-75

**(215)** 6" tall and adorable is ***Henny Penny***. Not only is she very rotund and can therefore hold a lot of coins, she also was made as a planter and comes in at least one other color combination. She has a '**P**' painter's mark.
Estimated value: $70-85

**(216)** Here is ***Butch,*** identical to the one above except for the inscription. It was painted for sale probably at one of the Las Vegas Casinos as a special order. It is possible that these could have been sold at other gift stores as well as we have found another ***Butch*** like this that reads "For My Mink".
Estimated value: $60-75

**(217)** ***Stinkie Bank*** is 7" tall and has a coin slot in the top of his head. He also has a cork in his base. This one is not incised and has no stickers.
Estimated value: $60-75

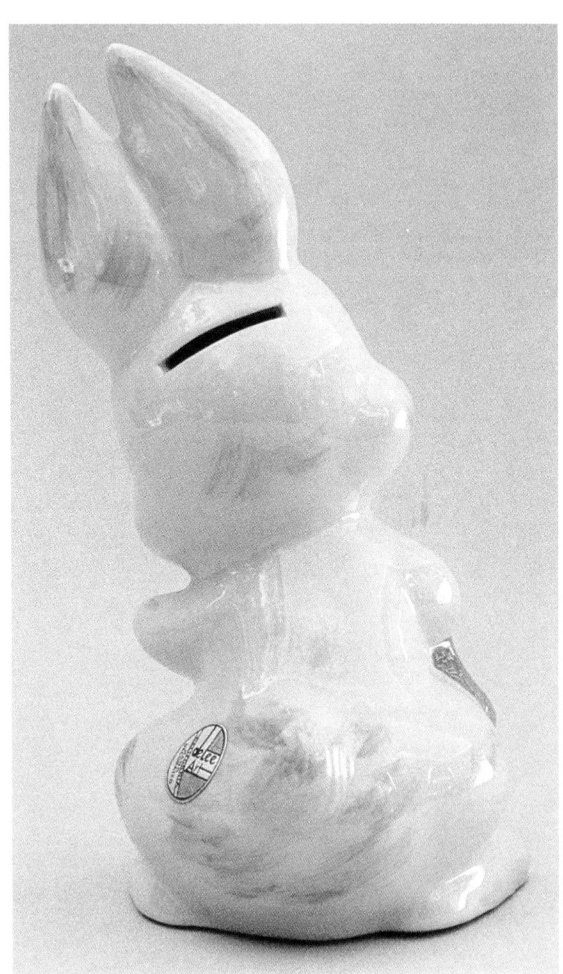

**(218)** 9" ***Money Bunny*** is a darling bank and is much sought after by collectors. She has her purse ready to go shopping. She has both her deLee sticker and her name plate.
Estimated value: $90-125

**(219)** 7" ***Peanuts*** is popular and difficult to find. ***Peaunts*** came as a bank and a planter. For the planter version, the drum top is wide open. For the bank, there is only a coin slot. It is difficult to see the slot in this photograph. He has an **'E'** painter's mark.
Estimated value: $75-100

**(220 and 221))** Two cute wall pocket/planters are ***P*** and ***U***. They are 5" tall with their deLee stickers on the back and their name plates on the front. They are incised 'deLee Art'. Of course, they are flat on the back.
Estimated value for the pair: $50-75

**(222)** This little guy was the single most popular item of the deLee Co. They sold about 100,000 of them, many through catalog sales. At one point, Jimmie Lee had 3 other ceramic factories making them just to keep up with the demand. ***DeStinker*** is about 5" tall. His matches were struck on the rough surface under his feet. He was very handy before the advent of room deodorizers. His poem reads:

If your bathroom is occupied
By someone who's a thinker
I hope he burns a match of mine
And makes me be DE STINKER

The deLee address is on the back of the tag.
Estimated value: $20-35
(with tag $30-45)

Note the differences in sizes of ***DeStinker***. This is probably due to the fact that several different ceramic factories were making them for deLee Art.

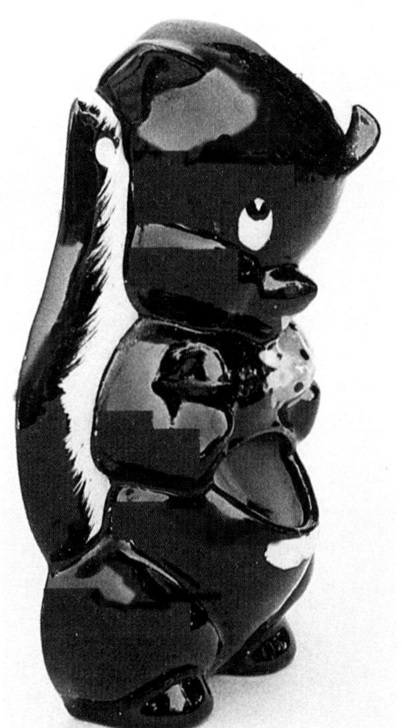

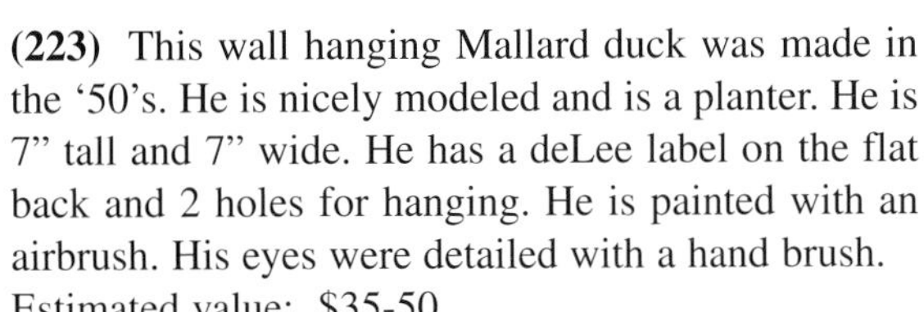

**(223)** This wall hanging Mallard duck was made in the '50's. He is nicely modeled and is a planter. He is 7" tall and 7" wide. He has a deLee label on the flat back and 2 holes for hanging. He is painted with an airbrush. His eyes were detailed with a hand brush. Estimated value: $35-50

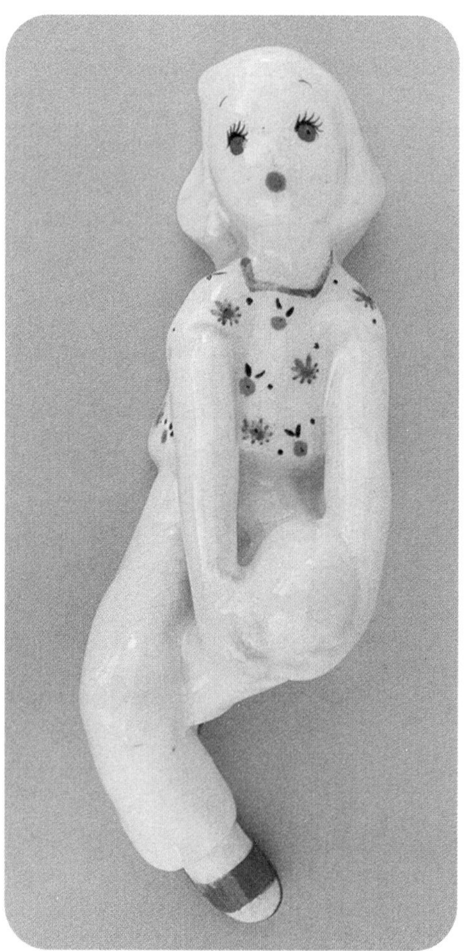

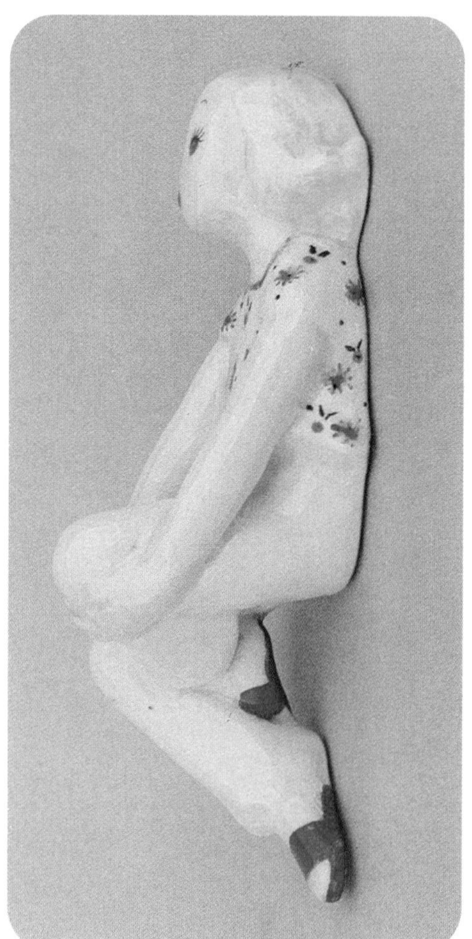

**(224)** This young girl wall plaque is a rare piece. She is 7" tall and has two holes on her flat back for hanging. She is wearing the play clothing of 1940's children. We suspect that there may be a matching boy wall hanging. She is incised 'deLee 40 USA'.
Estimated value: $75-100

**(225)** Another difficult to find piece. This spoon holder is 5" high and 7½" wide. It is unmarked. The flower painting matches ***Butch***, the piggy bank and grease pot.
Estimated value: $35-50

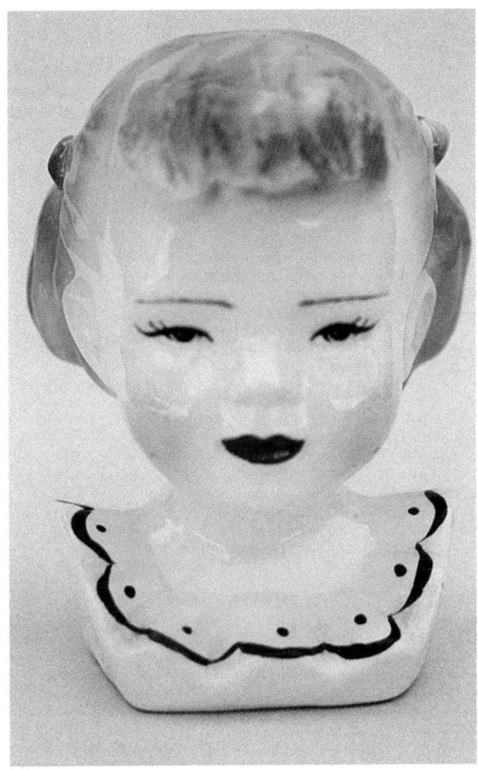

**(227)** This little girl head vase, 5½" high, was made in the '50's. She has the later deLee mark, a round circle with deLee Art written inside (see page 33). She is a combination technique of airbrushing and brush painting. Estimated value: $65-85

**(226)** This unique shelf sitting planter was modeled by Jimmie Lee for her daughter, Mary Jo, who was serving in the Navy at the time. These were made in production as well. She is 7" tall and is unmarked. Estimated value: $75-100

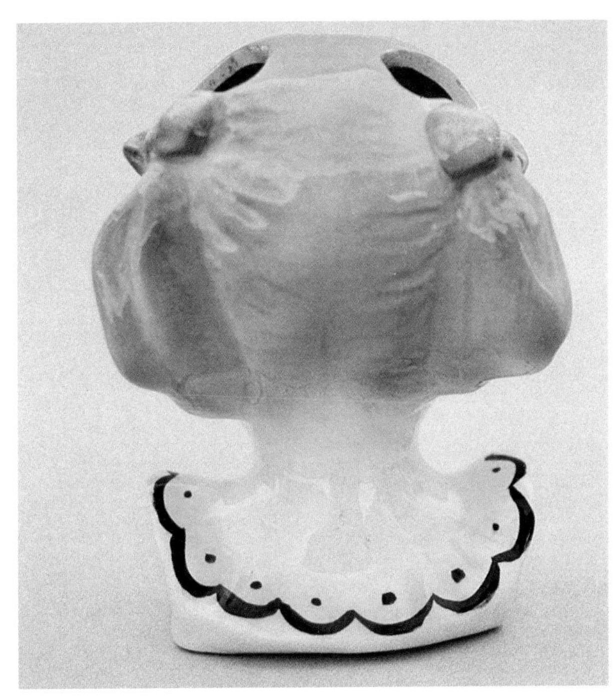

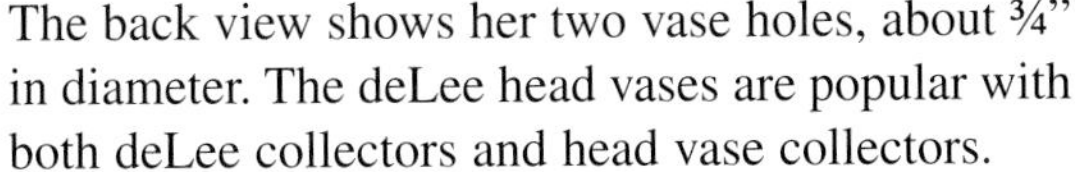

The back view shows her two vase holes, about ¾" in diameter. The deLee head vases are popular with both deLee collectors and head vase collectors.

**(228)** Shown here are four different hair colors of the same head vase. This classic 1940's lady was designed to hold Bobby pins, hence her name, ***Bobby PinUp***. Bobby pins were used profusely in the 30's and 40's. She is 3½" high. Many people feel that she looks like Lucille Ball.
Estimated value: $60-90

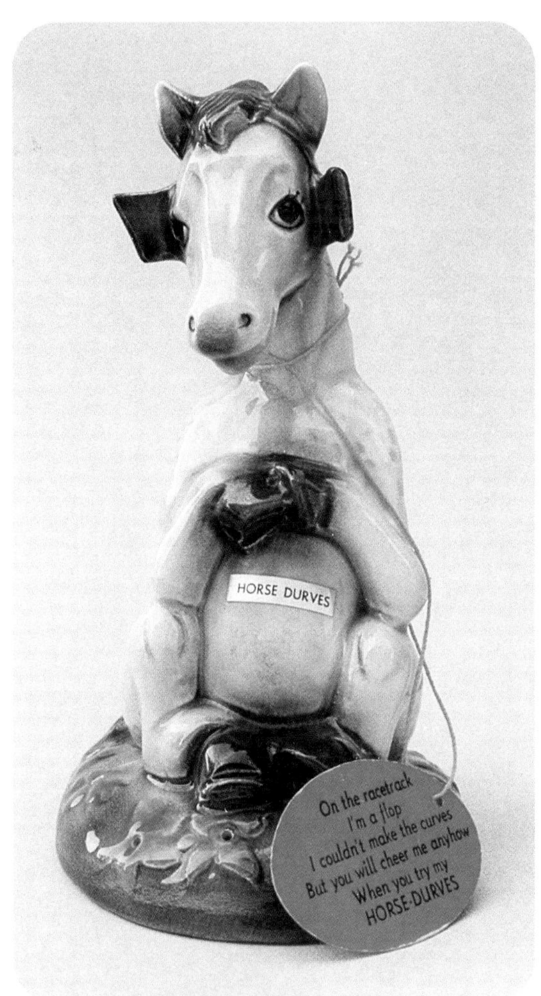


**(229)** 7" tall ***Horse Durves*** is quite a funny character. He came originally sitting on the hors d'oeuvres plate as shown. Most of the horses, who also have holes for toothpicks around the base, have become separated from this plate now. He is incised with the same mark as the plate below, right. The poem on his red tag reads:

"On the racetrack I'm a flop
I couldn't make the curves
But you will cheer me anyhow
When you try my HORSE-DURVES"

Estimated value without plate: $75-100
(with plate): $100-150

The later deLee mark shows clearly on the back of the plate. This mark was adopted in the 1950's.

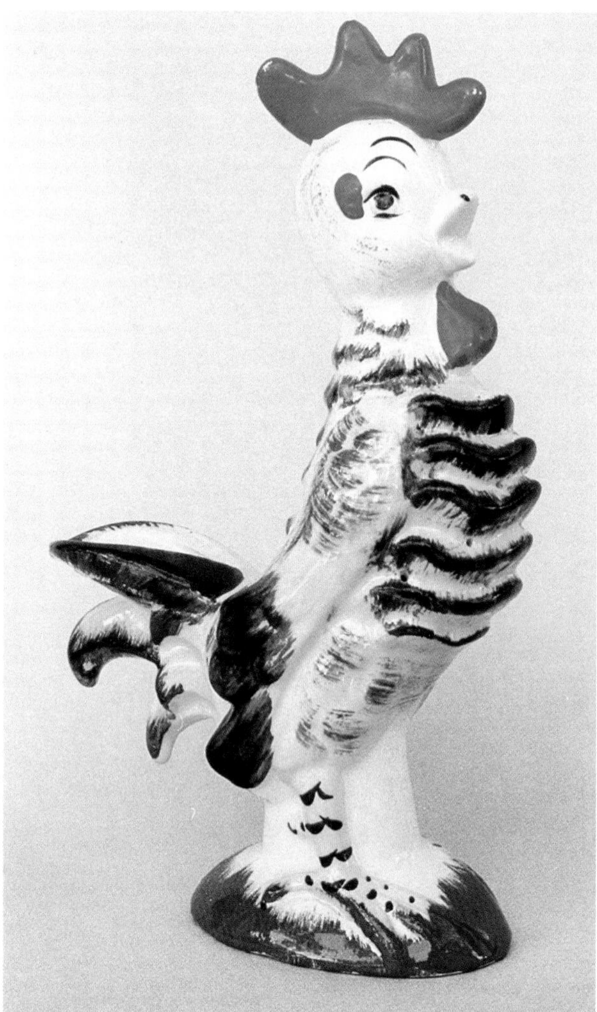

**(230)** This 10" rooster also originally came with an hors d'oeuvres plate. The plate is very similar to the one with ***Horse Durves***. There are many toothpick holes on rooster's chest. The red paint was applied after firing and is now rubbing off. His tail forms a vase/planter.
Estimated value without plate: $35-50
(with plate): $75-100

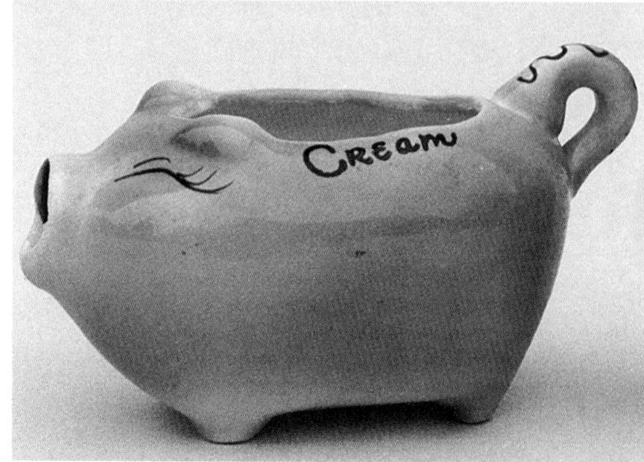


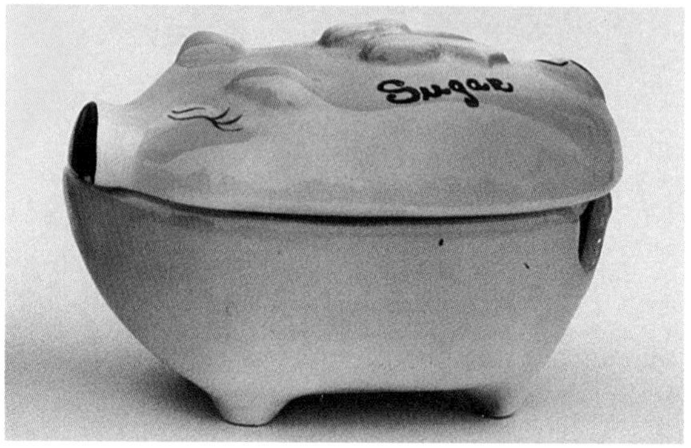


**(231 and 232)** This cream and sugar pair is a simplified version of the earlier pig. The 3" high set is airbrushed with some detailed hand painting. They are lacking some of the charm and detail of the earlier pieces. They are incised 'deLee Art Calif 1957' (creamer) and '1956' (sugar).
Estimated value for the pair: $35-45

**(233)** To meet the smoker's market of the day, deLee produced this ashtray with one of the series of tiny skunks on the rim. As is shown, his tail formed a match holder. The ashtray is about 5" in diameter. The ashtray is incised 'deLee Art'.
Estimated value: $45-60

12" tall ***Cookie*** was made as a boy and a girl. The modeling was different for each.

Estimated value each: $250-400

**(234)** Above is ***Cookie*** girl. She has a different chef's hat and is wearing a skirt. Her apron is painted with words while the boy's apron is plain.

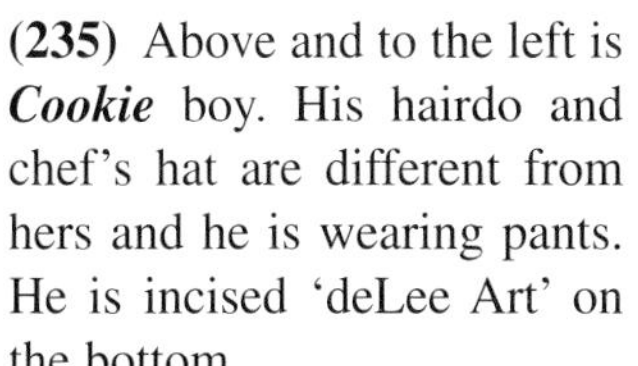

**(235)** Above and to the left is ***Cookie*** boy. His hairdo and chef's hat are different from hers and he is wearing pants. He is incised 'deLee Art' on the bottom.

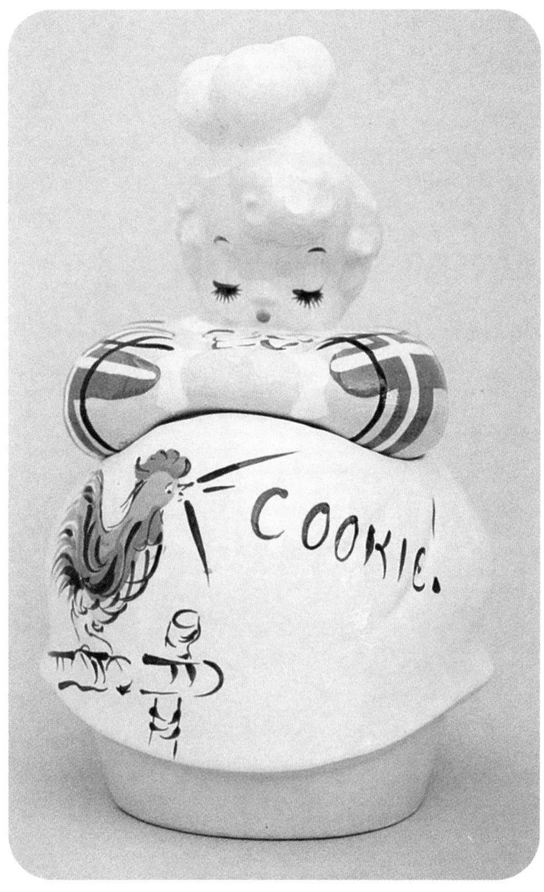


Another painted version of ***Cookie***. This is the girl. We have only found decoratively painted aprons, such as with strawberries, on the girls. Below, you see the painting inside this jar of the words, "ALL GONE".

The backside of ***Cookie***, the girl.

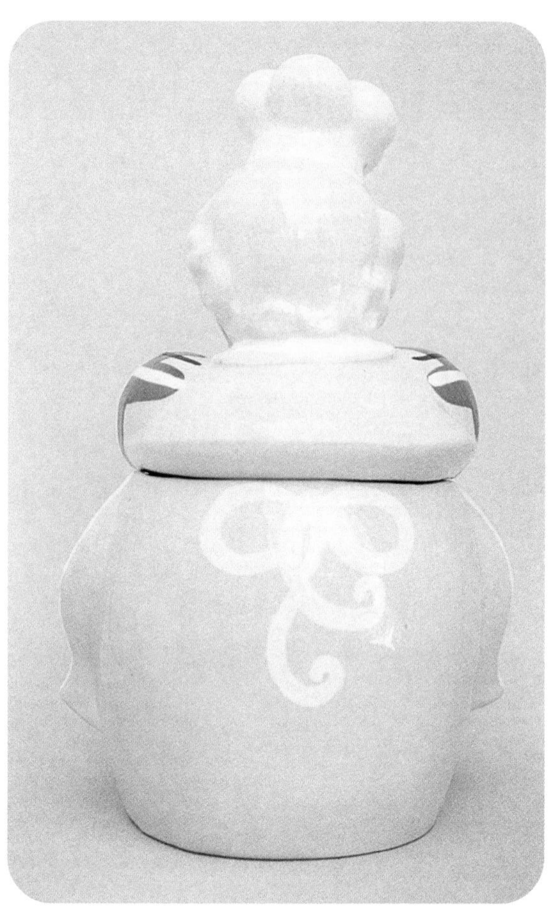

Recently found is an 8½" tall senorita with a big skirt, apron and hands clasped in front. She is split in two pieces like this cookie jar. But, since she is smaller, she was meant to hold candy.

**(236)** Another example of using the same mold to create something with a different use. Here is ***Butch***, the piggy bank, masquerading as a grease pot. While in the green ware stage, the piggy bank mold was cut horizontally thus making it a container. The inside was then completely glazed and fired so that grease could be safely poured into it. ***Butch*** was paired with salt and peppers named ***Wiggles*** and ***Giggles*** to make a kitchen set. The big pig is 5" high and 6" long. The little guys are about 3½" tall.
Estimated value for grease pot: $50-75

**(237 and 238)** A closer view of ***Wiggles*** and ***Giggles,*** the salt and pepper shakers who were described on the preceding page. ***Wiggles*** holds salt and ***Giggles*** holds pepper.
Estimated value each: $35-50

**(239 and 240)** A darling pair of shakers, ***Salty*** and ***Peppy***. They are 5" tall and have the round deLee sticker on their backs. They were made in the late 1940's.
Estimated value each: $45-65

**(241 and 242)** To complete the trio are 4" tall ***Sniffy*** and ***Snuffy***. ***Sniffy*** holds salt and ***Snuffy***, pepper. They are more of the charming skunks made by deLee.
Estimated value each: $35-45

Recently found too late to photograph is ***Pee Wee Bear*** (page 112) as Salt and Pepper shakers. He sports a "P" or "S" on his chest.

**(243)** To the left is a lamp featuring the ***Joanne*** figurine. We do not believe that this lamp was professionally made by a lamp company. It appears to have been "put together" at home, using lamp parts. Nevertheless, it made a charming boudoir lamp.
Estimated value: $60-80

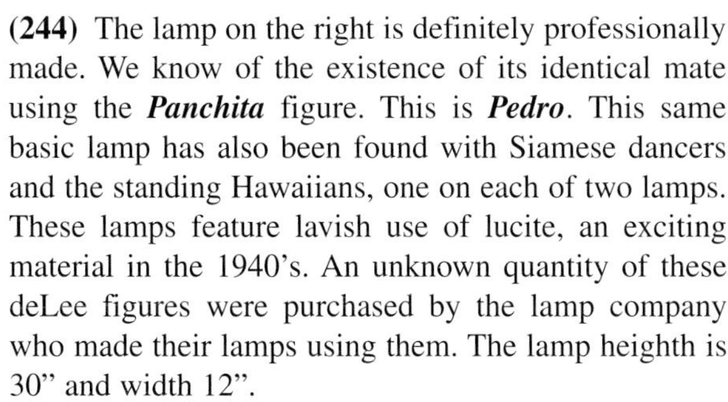

**(244)** The lamp on the right is definitely professionally made. We know of the existence of its identical mate using the ***Panchita*** figure. This is ***Pedro***. This same basic lamp has also been found with Siamese dancers and the standing Hawaiians, one on each of two lamps. These lamps feature lavish use of lucite, an exciting material in the 1940's. An unknown quantity of these deLee figures were purchased by the lamp company who made their lamps using them. The lamp heighth is 30" and width 12".
Estimated value: $75-90

**(245)** This cute little girl sitting on a flower frog is vintage early deLee. The whole piece is 5½" high and 4¾" long. She has no markings at all, just a classic deLee look. Estimated value: $90-125

**(246)** This darling little girl is leaning over the edge of a flower petal vase. The vase is 3½" in diameter and 2½" tall. The little girl is 5" tall. The piece has no markings but is unmistakenly deLee.
Estimated value: $75-125

# Other Figures Marketed By deLee

It was noted earlier that there are exceptions to the fact that Jimmie Lee modeled every piece of deLee Art. It is important for collectors to know these exceptions.

In the early 1950's, an artist previously unknown to Jimmie Lee, came to the deLee factory with a group of 12 Siamese cats that she had modeled. The artist was unable to secure financing to produce them herself and offered the master molds for sale to Jimmie Lee. It was becoming increasingly important at this time for the deLee Co. to add products to their line and thus the decision was made to purchase this group of molds. The cats were very well modeled and the molds were good. As far as can be remembered, all 12 cats were made for several years.

One departure from the deLee "norm" was that these cats were finely airbrushed. They all left the factory with silver deLee stickers on them. The cats are in several different sizes and many poses, standing, sitting and lying down. They range in size from 3" to 13" tall. Examples can be found here and on pages 88-89.

An equal number of this set of cats is found with the Brad Keeler mark. At this time, the only plausible explanation is that both deLee and Keeler were sold the same molds and neither company was told that duplicates were sold to any other company.

The second exception involved a business transaction only. One day, probably in the late 1940's, an artist arrived at the factory with completed ceramic pieces. She asked if Jimmie Lee could buy them from her at a discount and resell them wholesale to the retail stores, acting as her distributor. Jimmie Lee liked the quality of the work and agreed to sell them for this artist. The currently known pieces of this group are shown on page 138. They are a large chicken and rooster, and small chicks. They carry the deLee round sticker and name labels.

The rooster's name is Sylvester. Jimmie Lee does not remember how many different figures were in this group, possibly 6-10. After a few months, the deLee accountant counseled Jimmie Lee not to continue with this product. The discount and wholesale prices allowed no profit margin because the other artist insisted on setting the prices. As a result, this business arrangement ceased and the artist went elsewhere to sell her product. These figures have also been found with another company's label on them.

There exists a third, small group of figures that is a mystery to everyone, including Jimmie Lee herself. Examples of this group are; a dramatic bull, a bulky old fashioned telephone decorated with cherries and a turquoise pigeon. All of the pieces bear the correct silver deLee sticker. Jimmie Lee has no recollection of any of them but surmises that they were modeled by others and briefly added to the deLee line to increase their products. She is quite sure that she did not model them.

**(247)** A 9½" Siamese cat from the collection of 12 molds purchased by deLee from another artist. This cat has a deLee sticker.
Estimated value: $75-95

**(248)** Jimmie Lee does not remember creating this 6" bird but several have been found bearing the deLee sticker and in several colors. It was definitely in the product line.
Estimated value: $35-50

**(249)** A 7" bull clearly displaying his deLee sticker. Jimmie Lee does not remember who sculpted this bull but does remember making them at the factory for a short time.
Estimated value: $45-60

**(250)** Jimmie Lee knows for sure that she did not create this piece and several other items with this same look with the cherries added. They all have the deLee sticker so were clearly sold through the company but not made by them. To survive in the 1950's, companies had to augment their product line.
Estimated value: $25-35

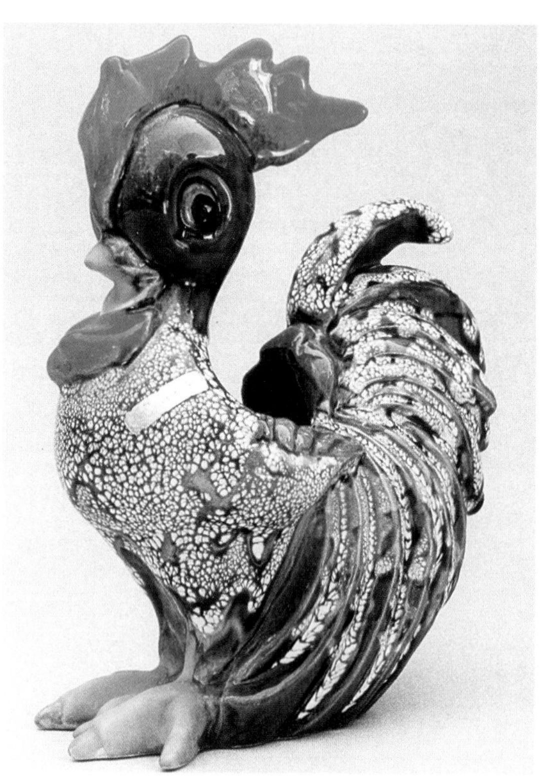

(252)

**(251)** These are several pieces from the group of chickens completely finished and sold wholesale to deLee. This marketing situation did not continue very long as it was not financially successful for the deLee Company. The rooster above is ***Sylvester.*** Notice that the red paint is applied under the glaze, something that was not done at deLee. They range in size from 4 - 9".
Estimated value: $35-50

(253) (254)

# Unauthorized Reproductions And Look Alikes

From the late 1940's on, deLee Art was plagued by unauthorized reproductions coming on the market at half the price of the real thing. The deLee Company was not alone. All of the successful contemporary ceramic companies were facing the same problem that ultimately put them all out of business by 1965.

There was no way for the deLee company to stop the production of these copies because Jimmie Lee didn't have the time or financial wherewithal to fight pirates and international agreements were much weaker then. A pirate merely bought an original, sent it to a reproduction factory where a mold was made from it and copies produced.

The reproduced pieces are usually not the same size as the original because clay shrinks differently depending on the materials used in the clay and the temperature at which it is fired. In many cases, the quality of the painting was hurried and poor but the buying public didn't seem to care. We have found many different deLee designs reproduced. These unauthorized reproductions were made by Oriental and American companies alike.

There is also a strong possibility that some of the copied deLee molds were sold to the amateur, hobby ceramic market. There have been many poorly executed, amateurish deLees found that were clearly done by loving hands at home.

Look alike figures are a different matter. In this case, the designs are not directly stolen from an original piece. These are figures that have been modeled from scratch by an artist, but are clearly in the style and design of deLee Art. To be kind, in some cases the modeler may have been unconsciously influenced, but some of the time it appears that the close copy is intentional. Many of these look alike figures are well done, colorful pieces in their own right.

As a deLee collector, it is important not to be fooled by unauthorized reproductions and look alike figures. Be sure that you understand what you are buying regardless of what anyone tells you. Study the photos in this book carefully since this will help you become more informed. We have spoken with some disappointed collectors who found out that some of their deLee figures are not genuine. There is absolutely nothing wrong with buying a reproduction as long as that is your informed intention and the price is right.

This unauthorized reproduction is from the real ***Ferdinand*** mold, shown below left. Notice that a flower was added in his mouth to make it appear to be a different figure. This reproduction was then placed on a flower frog base.

The bull on the right is the same unauthorized ***Ferdinand*** reproduction without the flower frog base. DeLee did not ever mold a flower in the bull's mouth. The bull on the left is the genuine deLee.

What is really striking about these poorly done unauthorized reproductions is the eyes. You can see that when eyes are badly painted, it really removes all the charm from the figure. Herein lies the genius of deLee. Also notice that the stripes are just two blocky swipes of the brush with no skunk character built in.

On the left is deLee's ***Pedro*** and on the right is a very small reproduction of of him.

On the left is deLee's Nina. It is uncertain if the reproduction on the right is a professional or an amateur effort. Like many of the others, it is smaller.

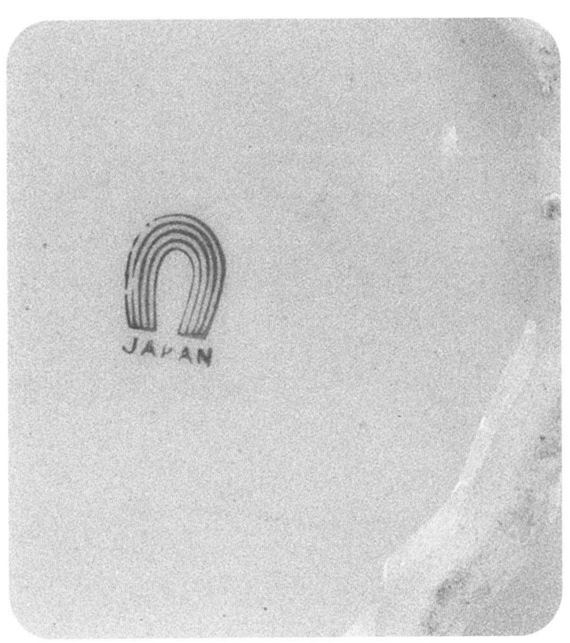


Again, on the left is deLee's ***Lizzie*** and on the right is the Japanese copy with its stamped mark on the bottom shown on the right. The Japanese piece was taken right from the original piece. The figure is airbrushed and the skirt design is stamped on with a rubber type stamp.

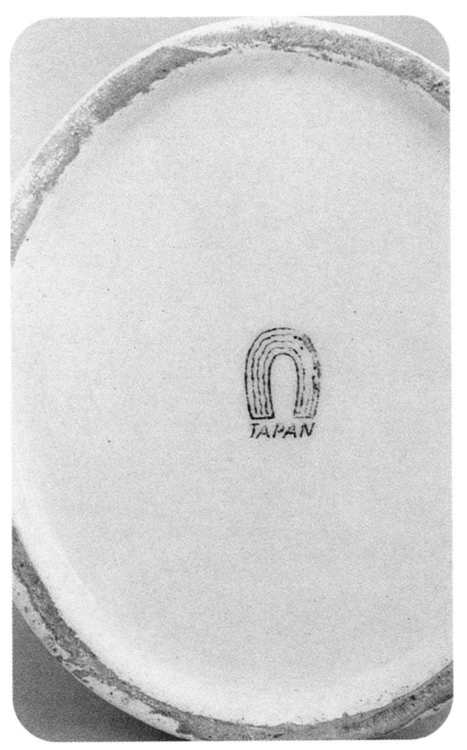

The girl on the right is trying to match her deLee original on the left as closely as possible. Not only is she taken off the original mold, but there is an attempt to mimic the painting technique as well. Her base is at left.

deLee's ***Daisy*** on the left is matched with her unauthorized copy on the right. The copy is mostly spray painted with a stamped design on her bodice and skirt. Her eyelashes are too exaggerated. She is stamped with the same Japan stamp as on page 141.

We believe that this is an example of the ***Maria*** mold that was sold to the amateur ceramic market. She was painted by a beginner at home.

Another example of the ***Panchita*** mold poorly done by an amateur.

In this example, the deLee ***Hans*** is on the right and the copy on the left. The copy is unmarked but painted much better than most. One big difference is that he does not have any flower ornamentation. The blue color is off as well.

This page shows examples of "look alikes." None of these are from the deLee molds. They were modeled by someone who was obviously influenced by deLee figures to the point of using the eyelash trademark of deLee. These figures were (and possibly still are) being produced commercially. They are unmarked.

# Care, Repair And Preservation Of The Figures

The most important and obvious fact about these ceramic figures is that they are BREAKABLE. They were produced, as are most ceramics, in a low fire kiln method which makes them more susceptible to cracking and chipping than a high-fire porcelain figure.

Fortunately, fired clay is not susceptible to many of the environmental damage problems such as air pollution and insects that plague other fine collectibles. The fired-on colors are permanent and will not fade over time.

The only time that the color red was used on a deLee piece was when it was painted on after the piece was glost fired and therefore it can be rubbed and/or washed off easily.

Glass fronted display cabinets are the very best method of keeping your collection safe and clean. Over time, dust will seep into the cabinets and your pieces will need to be dusted.

When possible, avoid using water when cleaning your figures. The pieces have undergone subtle changes over the last 50 years and they have become more porous. **Never** fill the planters with water. The water can seep under the glaze and combine with the clay causing ugly water marks and ruining the piece. The paper labels and their glue are very brittle now and can be ruined after being subjected to a water soaking.

If you acquire a new addition to your collection that is very dirty, dampen a soft cloth and carefully clean the piece, avoiding the use of harsh cleaning substances. After the figure is initially cleaned, it should only need dusting in the future.

The most difficult part of a deLee to clean is the more than 40 year old residue of dirt in the planters. It appears that many people did use the figures as planters as opposed to merely filling them with water for fresh flowers. It seems impossible to remove all the dirt as it has almost become part of the ceramic now. The safest cleaning method is the following. Use a small, soft brush, like an old toothbrush and either denture toothpaste or regular toothpaste with baking soda and peroxide added, and gently brush the inside of the planter. A cotton swab works well for tight spots. You can quickly swish some water around inside to clean out the residue. Do not leave the water inside! Pat the inside dry with a soft cloth.

If you must store all or part of your collection, always wrap each piece separately in Butcher paper or a bubble wrap type material. Never wrap an antique or collectible item in newspaper. The inks transfer to the piece and the paper has a very high acid content, all of which is very damaging. Make sure that the boxes used for transfer and storage are sturdy and have solid bottoms.

To repair or not is always a controversial subject in collecting. One assumes that people buy and collect old items because they like them and that their value is a secondary issue. Ceramic pieces do chip and crack easily and many of them need small repairs. deLee figures are becoming more scarce so having a figure professionally repaired is a good idea. Some will argue that a repair lowers the value, but a damaged piece has little value as well.

The most important aspect of repair is to have the job done by a qualified, professional restorer. Try to find a friend who has had a successful experience with repair work and can recommend someone in your area. If you need to find a professional through the Yellow Pages, go and visit his/her shop first. Ask to see their work which they should be happy to show you. Evaluate the work before leaving your figurine for repair.

The deLee Art Company did not make large numbers of figures and each year more disappear from breakage and disregard. Today's collectors are the current caretakers of these charming figures, whose sole purpose is to delight and brighten your life. Above all, collect, clean, restore and love them as only you can.